*A practical, helpful way to
maintain a healthy weight
after weight loss surgery.*

EAT IT UP!

The Workbook

by CONNIE STAPLETON, PH.D.
AUTHOR OF EAT IT UP! AND THRIVING!

Publisher's Note

This publication is designed to provide accurate and authoritative information in regard to subject matter covered. It is sold with the understanding that the publisher is not engaged in rendering psychological, financial, legal, or other professional services. If expert assistance or counseling is needed, the services of a competent professional should be sought.

Published by **Mind Body Health Services, Inc.**
www.mindbodyhealthservices.com

ISBN: 978-0-578-13946-3
Library of Congress Control Number: 2014905399
Printed in the USA

Dedication

To my good friend, Sine Gunn-Goldfinch, and everyone who has known and suffered the miseries associated with obesity; for those who are ready to put forth the necessary effort to healthfully manage their weight - and every area of their lives… this workbook was created for you. **Eat It Up!**

Acknowledgments

There is no question as to the five people who deserve all the credit for getting this workbook completed! If it weren't for them, these pages may never have been printed. How amazing it is that these five people are also some of my favorite human beings on the planet! When I think about the amount of time, effort and energy they put into this project, it genuinely astonishes me and reinforces the statement my business partner in A Post Op & A Doc, Cari De La Cruz and I always say, "No one can do this for you, but you can't do it alone!" We say that in reference to weight loss, but it clearly applies to other areas of life, as well! No one could have written this workbook for me, but I most certainly wouldn't have gotten it printed on my own!

Speaking of Cari De La Cruz, she is the first person I want to thank for the effort she put into this workbook. Cari did the formatting for the entire project, which is one little word that actually represents tons of work and many, many hours! It's really her love and patience and willingness to join me in sharing honest and sometimes difficult feedback with one another, as well as the lessons she helps me learn and the gifts she brings to our friendship and partnership for which I most thank her. Many hugs, friend! And thank you for being my partner in such a worthwhile venture as ours!

To Sine Gunn-Goldfinch, I owe a tremendous "thank you" for being my most "distant" friend, who, in spite of being half of a globe away, can see me clearly, inside and out. More thanks for the contributions you made to this workbook by your thorough editing and suggestions, and for your insights into the hearts and minds of those for whom this book is written. You are a treasure, my friend.

Our daughter Kelsey deserves thanks from me every single day for her dedication. Kelsey worked on this project with the same positive attitude, attention to detail and beneficial suggestions as she has for every project she helps me with (which are often thrown at her several at a time)! Thank you for all of your hard work, precious woman, for the privilege of getting to work with you every day, and for sharing your family with us on the weekends, as well! I love you so!

Many thanks to our son, Steven, who somehow manages to accomplish every task we send his way within hours of receiving them! Thank you for your talent, your willingness to share your honest opinion, providing your knowledge of technical things we are too ancient to tackle, and for taking the time from your hundreds of other projects to help us reach our always-at-the-last-minute-deadlines. I love you so!

Of course I thank our other daughter, Erin, who, although she probably didn't even know the rest of us were working on this project, is just as involved in our family and our love! I love you so!

There is not enough thanks for my Lovebug, Steve, who honestly does everything (except for the part I do while sitting on my hiney in my rocker with my computer in my lap), unless, of course, I'm working on my computer as it sits atop the "work station" (piece of plywood secured with thin wire) on my treadmill! Lovebug makes all the calls regarding printing, shipping, obtaining legal documentation, being liaison between all of those listed above, conveying messages, managing every detail, and, all the while, giving me loving hugs every time we pass by one another. He supports me, listens to me whine as well as shriek with glee, and reminds me when I forget, all of the reasons we stay up half the night to do the work we do – together. Thank you for being my Lovebug for Life and for being an equal partner in the work we do in the world of Recovery! I love you so!!

Oh, yeah – one final acknowledgment. Rod Hetzel – thank you! Thank you for being my bleepity, bleepity, bleepity, bleep friend! I love you, too!

Table of Contents

Table of Contents

Table of Contents

Chapter 1
FULLY FORWARD

Choosing to have bariatric surgery is, or was, one of the most important decisions you'll ever make. I wrote **Eat It Up!** and now, this companion workbook to encourage and support you throughout the process of maintaining a healthy lifestyle following weight loss surgery. My hope is that both the book, and this workbook, will provide you with the knowledge and skills to help ensure your long-term success in sustaining weight loss, maintaining improved health and enjoying your favorite activities with the people you love!

I often compare preparing for weight loss surgery and preparing for a wedding as having many similarities. Couples who have been happily married for years and years know that having a solid, happy marriage requires hard work. There are rough times and smooth times. Times you do things even though you don't feel like it…you do what needs to be done because it will benefit the relationship. At times you wonder what you have gotten yourself into, but because you made the decision to get married, you persist in keeping true to your vows. In the end, those who stick it out are proud of what they have accomplished. They are confident that the benefits of their marriage far outweigh the struggles.

So it is with bariatric surgery. You embarked on the journey, as you should, starry-eyed, barely able to wait for **The Big Day**, and thrilled about the prospect of the honeymoon! You knew that "real life" would begin soon enough. Like young newlyweds who have found their life partner, you chose to have weight loss surgery, which you are certain will lead to your lifelong happiness. Having weight loss surgery meant a way for you to really and truly lose weight, and to you, that may have meant finally being happy. To be sure, there will be times after your surgery that you won't feel like following through with behavior that is good for you (exercise; refraining from dessert; completing food and exercise diaries.) Whether you recently had your surgery or are several years out from surgery, you can start these behaviors at any time! There is ALWAYS hope, so remember that today is a new day!

Use this book as a way to commit or re-commit to the process of recovering from obesity. You already know these behaviors are essential for your long-term goals of sustained weight loss and happiness. So if you were never informed of these tools, if you used them in the past but stopped at some point along the way, or if have been using these tools all along, this workbook is for you!

There will also be times in your recovery from obesity when you wonder what you have gotten yourself into, again, whether you are new to the world of weight loss surgery, or had your procedure done years ago. Remember to reaffirm your commitment to your health and happiness each and every day. Then persist in doing "the next right thing," whatever that is at the moment. In the end, like the couple that joyfully celebrates their 50th wedding anniversary, you will rejoice knowing you made the choice to have a healthy body, to live life fully and to Eat It Up!

The **Eat It Up! Workbook** is a guide to help you, from the day you have your surgery, through the ups and downs of daily life as a post-surgical patient, to enjoying successful long-term weight loss and a genuinely happy, balanced life. By completing the exercises in this book, I hope to further educate and inspire you so you maintain the weight you lose following your procedure. Or, if it is the case that you have re-gained some of your weight, then use this book to get yourself into practicing these healthy habits. It's truly never too late to begin again. Of course, you are the one who has to make the decision to complete these exercises and put into practice the information in this workbook- on a daily basis.

Before we move on, let's take a look at what your hopes and expectations for having weight loss surgery are (if you haven't yet had surgery) or were (if you've already had surgery). The following exercise will help you do just that!

WLS Hopes & Expectations

Think about what your hopes and expectations are/were related to having weight loss surgery. Don't worry whether these seem "realistic" or "rational" or "reasonable." Just let yourself write down whatever comes to your mind. There are no "right" or "wrong" answers to these questions. They are simply designed to help you learn more about yourself!

An expectation I had when making the decision to have weight loss surgery was:

_____

_____

_____

_____

Another expectation I had when deciding to have weight loss surgery was:

_____

_____

_____

An additional expectation I had when choosing to have weight loss surgery was:

_____

_____

_____

_____

Something I <u>hoped</u> (but didn't necessarily expect) having weight loss surgery would result in was: _____

_____

_____

_____

Something else I hoped (but didn't necessarily expect) having weight loss surgery would result in was: _____

_____

_____

_____

Another thing I hoped (but didn't necessarily expect) having weight loss surgery would result in was: _____

_____

_____

_____

Are you surprised by anything that you wrote above? It will be interesting for you to read your responses a few months or even years from now! It might even be surprising to read what you wrote just now compared to what you thought about these things before you had weight loss surgery! Write any surprising thoughts you had on the following lines:

_____

_____

_____

_____

All of the exercises in this book are designed to get you to think about your process, to recognize how your thoughts and behaviors change over time. You will change and grow as a person throughout your lifetime, as will those who do not have weight loss surgery. Chances are good, however, that you will experience many changes in a relatively short period of time in relation to your weight loss surgery. Some of those changes you may want to incorporate into your new life and some you may likely "try on for size" and decide they "don't fit" who you are. Your relationship with yourself and with others will very likely change in the years immediately following your weight loss, which means you are going to have to address the changes or choose to ignore them. My suggestion would be to use this time of change as an opportunity to improve all areas of your life, not just your health! Read on, and you'll understand more of what I mean.

Again, if you are years out from your weight loss surgery, do the exercises based on what happened as you lost weight and in terms of where you are currently. Use another binder or journal if you need additional room for your responses.

As you work through the exercises in this book, please keep in mind that weight loss surgery is only the beginning of the happy, balanced life you are seeking. Weight loss surgery changes the size of your stomach and in some cases, re-routes parts of the intestinal tract. It does nothing to address any "head" issues and will not change things like the following:

* Having cravings for the foods you love.

* The fact that fast food drive-thrus still exist on nearly every busy street corner in town.

* Your habits of going to the refrigerator/cupboards on a regular basis.

* Using food as a source of comfort, companionship, stress relief, etc.. to fill an emotional need.

* You don't usually feel "motivated" to exercise.

* Holidays come every year, and along with them, many food-related traditions.

* Society will remain food-based: commercials for food will remain on television, billboards will bombard you with larger-than-life-size pictures of tempting tasty treats, and the latest restaurant chains will come to a city near you.

Those are some of the reasons you need help to resist the powerful impact food has had in your life. The exercises in this book can encourage you to follow through with your resolve to live a healthier lifestyle – but only if you do the exercises, incorporate the lessons into your life, and practice some of them each and every day. You can't succeed long-term by wishing and hoping for health…

Wishin' and A-Hopin'

List (5) five things you <u>wish</u> having weight loss surgery would do you for that you know it cannot do:

1. _____

2. _____

3. _____

4. _____

5. _____

Being accurately aware of the things that the surgical procedure and your resulting stomach pouch cannot do for you is essential for your success! Look back on this list when you need to remind yourself of the fact that surgery cannot change certain things… no matter how badly you <u>wish</u> it could!

Reflections on this exercise

What have you become aware of while doing these exercises? Did you discover the wishes you had/have regarding WLS? Did you learn how you hoped WLS would magically change things for you? (And don't worry, everyone has had some magical thinking about what weight loss surgery could do.) The point is to be honest with yourself about things you wished surgery could do – even if, in your head, you knew it wasn't possible. Maybe you're disappointed in some of the aspects of the surgery and life afterward. That's ok, too! It's only by being honest with ourselves and acknowledging our truth, that we can be open-minded enough to accept the realities of life. Use this space to write down your thoughts about the exercises you have done so far. Remember, no one is going to read this (unless you choose to share it). This information is for your own personal growth. Be honest and let it all out!

_____

_____

_____

_____

_____

_____

_____

_____

_____

_____

_____

_____

_____

_____

_____

_____

_____

Bottom Line: Surgery does absolutely nothing to deal with the two things that are primarily responsible for a person's regaining of weight after bariatric surgery: 1) your long-term eating and exercise habits and 2) the cognitive and emotional issues related to those eating and exercise behaviors. The fact is, without addressing the cognitive, emotional and behavioral issues underlying obesity, weight loss surgery is actually a very expensive and invasive "diet." That is not why you elected to have weight loss surgery. So make a commitment NOW to complete this workbook and follow through with the suggestions for sustained weight loss.

Exercise: Reminding Myself

Part A: Although you've probably done (parts of) this exercise (many times, in fact) I'd like to suggest you do it again… although this time, we'll be adding an additional element or two, which will be important for you later in this book.

List prior diets you have been on in which you have lost at least 15 pounds and then complete the information requested for each "diet":

DIET 1.			
Year | Age Stage of Life	Amount of Weight Lost	Method (Diet)	Length of Time I Kept Weight Off
_____	_____	_____	_____

What motivated me to start the diet this time? _____

_____

_____

How long did it take me to lose this weight? _____

_____

_____

What happened that I started to regain my weight? _____

_____

_____

_____

How much weight did I regain and approximately how long did it take to regain it?

_____

_____

What might have prevented me from regaining my weight after stopping this diet?

_____

_____

_____

DIET 2.

Year | Age Stage of Life	Amount of Weight Lost	Method (Diet)	Length of Time I Kept Weight Off
_____	_____	_____	_____

What motivated me to start the diet this time? _____

_____

_____

How long did it take me to lose this weight? _____

_____

_____

What happened that I started to regain my weight? _____

_____

_____

_____

How much weight did I regain and approximately how long did it take to regain it?

_____

_____

_____

What might have prevented me from regaining my weight after stopping this diet?

_____

_____

_____

DIET 3.

Year | Age Stage of Life	Amount of Weight Lost	Method (Diet)	Length of Time I Kept Weight Off
_____	_____	_____	_____

What motivated me to start the diet this time? _____

_____

_____

How long did it take me to lose this weight? _____

_____

_____

What happened that I started to regain my weight? _____

_____

_____

_____

How much weight did I regain and approximately how long did it take to regain it?

_____

_____

_____

What might have prevented me from regaining my weight after stopping this diet?

_____

_____

_____

DIET 4.

Year | Age Stage of Life	Amount of Weight Lost	Method (Diet)	Length of Time I Kept Weight Off
_____	_____	_____	_____

What motivated me to start the diet this time? _____

_____

_____

How long did it take me to lose this weight? _____

_____

_____

What happened that I started to regain my weight? _____

_____

_____

_____

How much weight did I regain and approximately how long did it take to regain it?

_____

_____

_____

What might have prevented me from regaining my weight after stopping this diet?

_____

_____

_____

_____

DIET 5.

Year | Age Stage of Life	Amount of Weight Lost	Method (Diet)	Length of Time I Kept Weight Off
_____	_____	_____	_____

What motivated me to start the diet this time? _____

_____

_____

How long did it take me to lose this weight? _____

_____

_____

What happened that I started to regain my weight? _____

_____

_____

How much weight did I regain and approximately how long did it take to regain it?

_____

_____

What might have prevented me from regaining my weight after stopping this diet?

_____

_____

_____

Part B: What are some common denominators related to the reasons I regained my weight when I "went off the diet" (be specific). For example, don't write, "I returned to old habits." Instead, list the "old habits," such as "*I regained weight because I stopped exercising. I regained weight because I allowed myself to eat chips and spaghetti and to drink sugary sodas daily."*

After I "went off" these diets, I regained my weight because: _____

_____

_____

_____

_____

_____

_____

Part C: List 3 to 5 reasons (specific, serious reasons rather than "magical thinking" or "wishful fantasies") you chose to have weight loss surgery. (I know this is close to what you wrote in the prior exercises, but indulge me...). Your responses to this specific question will be important throughout the rest of this workbook.

I chose to have weight loss surgery for the following reasons:

1. _____

_____

2. _____

_____

3. _____

_____

4. _____

_____

5. _____

_____

Part D: Using your responses to previous sections of this exercise, write the answers to the following sentence stem so that it personalizes this for you and makes it crystal clear how your behaviors and your goals are related.

1. If I return to _____,

   (list a previous behavior that led to weight regain from Parts A/B of this exercise)

   I am less likely to _____

   _____

   _____.

   (list one of your reasons for having WLS from Part C of this exercise).

2. If I return to _____,

   (list a previous behavior that led to weight regain from Parts A/B of this exercise)

   I am less likely to _____

   _____

   _____.

   (list one of your reasons for having WLS from Part C of this exercise)

3. If I return to _____,

   (list a previous behavior that led to weight regain from Parts A/B of this exercise)

   I am less likely to _____

   _____

   _____.

   (list one of your reasons for having WLS from Part C of this exercise)

4. If I return to _____,

   (list a previous behavior that led to weight regain from Parts A/B of this exercise)

   I am less likely to _____

   _____

   _____.

   (list one of your reasons for having WLS from Part C of this exercise)

That series of exercises was to help you recognize the expectations you had in regard to having weight loss surgery, to look at any magical thinking you may have had about what surgery could and could not do for you, and finally, to help you define your specific, unique reasons for wanting to have weight loss surgery. The final exercise was to have you identify the specific behaviors you engaged in that resulted in weight regain after prior successful efforts to lose weight. That's right – I said successful. Even though you may have thought those previous diets were "failures," you did lose weight on them, so you had to have changed some behavior(s) in order to do so. You then regained weight because you resorted to doing something that led to regain. The point is – if you return to those same behaviors you listed above, you are likely to get the same result: weight regain – even after weight loss surgery. I had you pair up your reasons for weight loss with the behaviors that led to weight regain so you can make the connection between the unhealthy behavior and your not having what you want in life as it relates to your weight.

Bottom line? As they say in recovery circles, "If you always do what you always did, you'll always get what you always got." Wanna keep that weight off? Then you gotta stay away from those things you listed that resulted in your weight regain. Yep – I've said it before and I'll say it many more times - even though you had weight loss surgery.

We want to focus on the positive! You chose to have weight loss surgery for the reasons you wrote above. The goal is to help you keep your weight off for the rest of your life so you can more fully enjoy your life. I am going to spend the rest of The Eat It Up! Workbook guiding you through the process of exploring the cognitive, emotional and behavioral components that ultimately determine your success in sustaining your weight loss - so you won't have spent thousands of dollars on yet another "failed diet." If you do the exercises in this workbook there is every hope you will reach the goals you have set. Beyond that, you will experience the transition from a world that has been like an old television show experienced in only black and white to a life that is exploding in full, brilliant color! The difference is indescribable. The choice is yours.

Notice in the above paragraph I did not say "you will reach the weight goals you have set." There's a specific reason for my word choice. Although the physicians you work with may concern themselves with specific weight goals, my hope is that you will turn your attention away from goals that have numbers affiliated with them (a number on the scale, the number that is the size of clothing you wear, the number of calories you consume in a day) to goals that are not number-related but are, instead, living-related. The reasons you listed in Part C of the previous exercise may be examples of goals for improved living related to your loss of excess weight.

The difference in number-related goals and living-related goals is important. If you don't reach a specific number on a scale or lose a specific number of pounds in a week or fit into a specific size of clothing, you may become frustrated, disappointed and may "feel like" a failure. However, if you focus on living-related goals and, for example, lose only twelve of the fifteen pounds you wanted to in a month, you may still be able to get up off the floor more easily after playing with your grandchild! NOW you feel like a success!

Non-Number Goals

List (5) five specific non-number goals you have for living that allow you to have a good quality of life and be free from weight-related medical problems:

1. _____

2. _____

3. _____

4. _____

5. _____

Your Whole Self

I take a whole person (mind/body/spirit) approach in my work. To me, addressing your whole person and all areas of your life following weight loss surgery translates to your permanently keeping off the weight you lose following surgery - and in finding greater happiness in your life. I do this by focusing on six major areas of your life, or Centers of Balance, which include your Physical Center, your Cognitive Center, your Emotional Center, your Social Center, your Spiritual Center, and your Enterprise Center.
Your Centers of Balance: Your True Keys to Happiness

The happiest, most functional people in our society live balanced lives. I describe a balanced life in terms of those six Centers of Balance. The happy, functional people I speak of spend time in solitude or prayer and carry the benefits into their lives while still dealing with "the real world" (Spiritual Center). They put effort into keeping their thoughts and feelings in a moderate range. They are not ruled by rigid thoughts or out-of-control emotions, nor are they emotionally shut down or blunted (Cognitive Center and Emotional Center). They spend time with friends, but not at the expense of their families or other responsibilities (Social Center). They get physical exercise on a regular basis and engage in physical activity, but don't take it to the extremes (Physical Center). They work, but don't overdo it. They give back to their communities through volunteer or service work, while taking care of themselves and their families or other responsibilities (Enterprise Center). My goal is to address your real-life issues following bariatric surgery in the context of your Centers of Balance. The result: you will live the well-balanced life of one of the genuinely happy people in our world in your new, more physically healthy body, keeping your weight off throughout your lifetime.

My Centers of Balance

For each of the **Centers of Balance**, fill in the associated box in each column using a scale of 1 – 10 to indicate how satisfied you are with the amount of attention and effort you put into each Center. (1 = Not at all satisfied; 10 = Perfectly satisfied).

	Spiritual	Cognitive	Emotional	Social	Physical	Enterprising
10						
9						
8						
7						
6						
5						
4						
3						
2						
1						

What areas would you like to put more effort into? What are your reasons for this?

_____

_____

_____

_____

_____

_____

What areas are getting more attention than you would like? In other words, are there areas of your life you are putting more effort into than you think is reasonable/healthy? What are your reasons for saying this?

_____

_____

_____

_____

_____

_____

_____

_____

_____

_____

Throughout the rest of this book, you will develop specific plans for working toward a healthier balance in your life by addressing each Center individually. Naturally, the focus will be on how each of these Centers of Balance is related to your goals for a healthy lifestyle. Before we move on, let's do a "just for the heck of it" exercise!

The Genie Game – just for fun!

Imagine a genie appears to you at this very moment. The genie wants to hear your three wishes in relation to each of your Centers of Balance. Don't worry if what you ask for seems outrageous, ridiculous or impossible. Just go with your first thoughts and let the genie know what you'd wish for!

Genie, In regard to my **Spiritual Center**, I wish:

1. _____

2. _____

3. _____

Genie, In regard to my **Cognitive Center** (the things I think and the way I think), I wish:

1. _____

2. _____

3. _____

Genie, In regard to my **Emotional Center**, I wish:

1. _____

2. _____

3. _____

Genie, In regard to my **Social Center**, I wish:

1. _____

2. _____

3. _____

Genie, In regard to my **Physical Center**, I wish:

1. _____

2. _____

3. _____

Genie, In regard to my **Enterprise Center** (the way I give back to others), I wish:

1. _____

2. _____

3. _____

Now, let's get moving! We've got lots of work to do in the upcoming chapters. I want to let you know ahead of time that some of the exercises in the workbook may stir up painful or difficult emotions. If you need to stop and put the work down for a day or two, then do just that. Work at your own pace. I strongly encourage people to enter therapy, even if there is nothing horrible going on in your life, currently – or in the past. Having someone neutral to talk to about the everyday issues in your life is wonderful. Having that sort of person to help you process your thoughts and feelings as you work through an emotional-laden issue like your obesity can truly help in a number of ways. If you do choose to go see a therapist as you work through this book, choose one who is experienced in either addiction work or family systems work. Just be sure you're comfortable with the person. The relationship you develop with them can be the most helpful part of the process anyway! Return to this workbook regularly. Do the exercises again at a later date and see what may have changed for you along the way!

One final thing before we move on to address each Center of Balance in terms of your maintaining a healthy lifestyle and balance in your life. A certainty about healthy recovery from obesity is this: No one can do this for you… but you can't do it alone. There are going to be many times you will need to enlist the help of people to support you when the going gets tough. In addition, you're going to have to be able to count on yourself at times to reach within and muster the strength to get through a difficult time.

Being prepared is one thing that will serve you well in your recovery from obesity. In just a few paragraphs we're going to have you develop a support team. Be sure to make a list of these people on your smart phone, your computer, and/or an index card you carry in your wallet so you can turn to them for firm and fair support when you need it. Have their phone numbers handy at all times!

Let me explain what I mean by "firm and fair support." I want you to teach your support team members what this means, as well, so they actually support you rather than unwittingly enable you! Being "firm" means to hold you accountable. You are the one who chose to have weight loss surgery so that you could enjoy improved health and a better quality of life. You were informed, somewhere along the process of preparing for surgery, that if you wanted to keep your weight off for the rest of your life, you were going to have to make healthy food choices and exercise. You knew these things. You agreed to these things. A "firm" support friend will gently remind you of this. If you are tempted to excessively eat junk food, chips, cake, go to fast food restaurants, drink sugary drinks and give up on exercising, a "firm" friend will let you know that if you choose to engage in those unhealthy behaviors, you will regain an unhealthy body and lifestyle.

The "fair" part comes in as compassion. In other words, your support person will be trained (by you) to be compassionate, while gently kicking you in the rear. They will acknowledge how hard it is to forego the treats when everyone else at the office partakes of them. They will kindly empathize that it is not fair that one of your burdens in life has been obesity. They will lovingly lament that you have had a hard day at the office, a nasty argument with your loved one, that the moon and the stars are not aligned, and then they will firmly remind you that none of those things are excuses to deviate from your healthy living plan. Get it?! I thought you would. So, be sure to coach your support team members on the "firm and fair" method of supporting you!

Determine your Support Team:

It's important to know who makes up your support team. There will be times you need support when you're at work. You may need support related to a situation with a co-worker or a boss. You may need support at work when there is a potluck meal and you are tempted to partake of foods that are not on your healthy eating plan. There could be times you are distracted by thoughts of the junk food in the vending machine and having someone to talk about it with would help. Perhaps you have a co-worker who would agree to walk with you during your lunch hour.

Who, at work, can I turn to when I need firm and fair support?

about work-related issues: _____

about food-related issues: _____

If there is no one at the work site I can count on for support in these areas, who can I call for support during my work hours if I need to?

Who, from my WLS family, can I turn to when I need firm and fair support?

_____

If no one from this group is available when I need them, who can I reach out to?

Who, in my family, can I turn to when I need firm and fair support:

about food and health issues: _____

about non-food, non-health issues: _____

If no one from this group is available when I need them, who can I reach out to?

_____

Here are (5) five healthy things I can do to provide support for myself when I choose to or when I am unable to find another person to help support me:

1. _____

2. _____

3. _____

4. _____

5. _____

All right! You've got your support team determined. You're prepared to teach them the "firm and fair" way of supporting you. And you have identified healthy ways to help yourself if you are unable to contact another person. That means it's time to move on!

Work hard and enjoy the process of learning more about yourself. Share what you learn with those who are closest to you so they can better understand what you're going through. Have them share how what you're doing applies in their own lives, even if it's not specifically related to food. You'll be enhancing your personal relationships and deepening your emotional levels of intimacy. All good stuff for endeavoring upon an even healthier recovery from obesity!

" My friends and family are my support system. They tell me what I need to hear, not what I want to hear and they are there for me in the good times and bad times. "

Kelly Clarkson

YOUR CUP RUNNETH DRY
Obesity & Your Centers of Balance

As you already know, various factors account for obesity. Let's take a quick review of them now. Take a few minutes to complete the exercises along the way to help you get a more thorough understanding of the origins of your obesity.

The Physiological Facts

Without a doubt, biological and medical factors play a role in obesity. Let's take a look at physiological factors that may have contributed to your weight issues.

Genetics

Medical facts indicate that genetics account for approximately one-third to one-half of the reason a person is overweight or obese.

Thyroid Problems

An underactive thyroid can be a contributing factor in weight gain.

Medication

A number of medications do result in weight gain. Certain prescription drugs used to treat mood disorders, seizures, migraines, diabetes, and even high blood pressure can cause weight gain. Some steroids, hormone replacement therapy, and oral contraceptives can also result in unwanted pounds.

Disease

Some illnesses, including hormone problems, depression and some rare diseases of the brain can lead to obesity.

Physiological factors which may have contributed to your obesity:

What family members in your immediate and extended family are obese?

_____

_____

_____

What medical illnesses do you, or have you had, that may have contributed to your obesity? _____

_____

What medications do you currently take or have you taken in the past that may have contributed to your obesity? _____

_____

The E Factors: Environment and Emotions

Environment

Dorothy Law Nolte, Ph.D. wrote a painfully true, insightful poem entitled *Children Learn What They Live*. Undeniably, children learn what they live in a home where one or more of the parents is obese. In fact, (sorry, moms) the number one determinant of childhood obesity is maternal obesity. Obese parents teach their children poor eating choices and habits. And so begins another generation of obese people.

What factors in your environment contributed to your obesity?
Check those that pertained to your life in the past (or in the present)!

_____ We ate/eat at fast food/other restaurants frequently.

_____ We ate/eat a lot of bread, pasta, rice, potatoes and other starches.

_____ We ate/eat a lot of gravies with food (on eggs, breads, meat, potatoes).

_____ We had/have a lot of junk food at our house (cookies, cake, ice cream, chips, snack crackers, desserts).

_____ We are/were required to eat all of the foods put on our plates.

_____ We often ate/eat a snack before bed.

_____ We seldom ate/eat breakfast.

_____ Breakfast (if it was/is eaten) is often sugary cereal, pancakes, grits, bagels and other non-nutritious food.

_____ We drank/drink a lot of sugary drinks, including fruit juice, soda, KoolAid.

_____ Butter was/is used liberally (on veggies, bread, pancakes, bagels, popcorn, etc.)

Put an asterisk or star in front of all of the environmental factors that are still problematic in your life that you can now influence in a positive way to make your life healthier.

List other environmental factors that had an impact on your obesity, either during your childhood or in your life at the present time: _____

_____

_____

_____

Keep in mind that, unlike heredity, over which we have no influence, our environment is something we can influence at this time in our lives. As a child, your life was fairly dictated by your parents/caretakers and you had little influence. Not so today! Your environment is the area in which you can make the most positive changes in terms of managing a healthy weight and lifestyle!

Emotions

Emotionally laden issues underlie a person's obesity. The emotional heartache associated with obesity is as painful as the knee and joint pain associated with carrying 100 excess pounds. The emotional heartache hurts as badly as the back and leg and lung pain that an obese person experiences when climbing a flight of stairs. The emotional pain feeds on itself. The shame, embarrassment, anger, and fear associated with being overweight fuels the low self-worth experienced by obese people. Their low self-esteem emerges as negative self-talk, self-destructive behavior, and self-punishment, which leads to intensified feelings of hurt, sadness, shame, and rage. It is a cycle that turns continually, like a paddlewheel beneath a waterfall. And, like the water rushing toward the fall, the pain never seems to end.

Your Life as a Cup

I can't write this workbook without including the awesome story about the cup! A person once told me, "My mother, on her death bed, told me that when I was born into this world, her mother, my grandmother, said I was a cup. My mother thought her mother was loony, yet gingerly asked what she meant. Grandma said that like every other child born into this world, I was born with a full cup, a fully 'authentic person.' I was full of all of the 'good stuff' I would need to be happy in this world. I was full of love and kindness, joy and self-esteem, wonder and delight, compassion and generosity, faith and wisdom. My parents' job, Grandma said, was to not spill a single drop from my cup."

"My mother then apologized to me for spilling my cup when I was a child. She explained that she spilled some of the good stuff from my cup any time she was critical of me, when she ignored my needs, and when she was too preoccupied to care for my needs. What I realized is that as I was raised, more and more of my cup was spilled - some by my parents and some by mean kids at school - and then the worst thing of all happened. I started dumping it out myself. I have been nearly empty for a long time. It's like being spiritually bankrupt. The more the 'good stuff' got poured out, the more I ate, trying to fill the cup back up. I got fat. I was no longer the person I was born into this world to be. Mom reminded me before she died that my 'authentic self' is still inside of me, a person created by God with a special purpose. She said she hoped I would try to find that person again."

"That's why I decided to have bariatric surgery. I wanted to find my authentic self. I wanted to get rid of the fat and find healthy ways to fill my cup again and be who I was meant to be. I've lost 85 pounds so far and am learning how criticism and teasing spilled the 'good stuff' from my cup, as did witnessing the animosity between my parents. When I got older, I hated myself and spilled even more by getting in and out of abusive relationships, dropping out of college three times and losing scholarships, and by putting on more and more weight. I was punishing myself. Now, as I am learning to fill my cup back up in healthy ways, I'm starting to like myself. I can see that I have unique gifts and talents, and I am excited about finishing my degree and starting to teach. I will finally be living the life I was meant to live. I am becoming my authentic self."

The Empty, Unbalanced Cup of Obesity

Every day I work with wonderful human beings who have unique talents and gifts, whose Cups were spilled in a variety of ways during childhood. Their authentic selves became hidden beneath layers of fat. Their lives become unbalanced as each individual Center of Balance is knocked off course. As a person's Cup is spilled, their Centers of Balance are tilted. The results are the same: the person begins to look outside himself to fix the emptiness within. The obese person chooses food. More and more food is needed because it never takes the pain completely away, no matter how much is eaten. The authentic person is hidden. Hidden behind the food and hidden behind the fat.

The Dumping and Refilling of Your Cup

By having bariatric surgery, you have taken a major step toward refilling your cup. Serious choices about if and how you choose to continue to refill your cup await you. The prize for doing so is finding your authentic self, who has hidden dormant inside you for a long, long time. Before the tools for helping you refill your cup are disclosed, we need to look more carefully at how it was dumped in the first place.

Imbalance resulting from neglect

When I talk with clients about how their cups were spilled, they often become quiet and distant. Very often people get defensive. Sometimes neglect occurs because of circumstances beyond anyone's control; no one has done anything "bad" or "wrong." The reality remains, however, that sometimes children don't get the sufficient amount of emotional attention they need to mature in optimally healthy emotional ways.

Intentional neglect

Neglect can be unintentional, but it can also be deliberate. When a parent chooses to leave the kids at home alone so she can go to the clubs, neglect is a deliberate choice. When parents are too caught up in their own careers, social lives, or partners to tend to their children's needs, neglect is a deliberate choice. Putting their own needs above the needs of their children is an indicator of the imbalance and emptiness on the part of the parents. The absence of adult attention and supervision in the lives of these children sucks the "good stuff" from their cups. Does this mean these parents are "bad" people or "bad" parents? Not necessarily. It does mean they are making parenting decisions that will adversely affect their children.

Examples of neglect include:

* not being fed nutritious food

* being left alone or with a babysitter much of the time

* being physically with a parent but the parent being overly focused on other people/activities (reading, on the phone, being on the computer, etc.)

* not being clothed appropriately (no warm clothes in the winter, etc.)

* medical or dental neglect

* educational neglect

* inadequate supervision – not being protected from hazards in the home, etc.

* lack of appropriate physical nurturing or affection

* lack of attention to hygiene

In order to fully recover from obesity, you have to be courageous enough to identify things that may have led to your eating for comfort. You've heard it before, and it's accurate: the truth shall set you free! List any examples of neglect you may have experienced in your childhood (remember, this is not about blaming anyone or implying your parents or other caregivers were "bad" people). In other words, try not to feel "guilty" because you think you are being hard on your parents or other caretakers who may have neglected you in some way.

_____

_____

_____

_____

Abuse

Research has shown that childhood sexual abuse is frequently a factor in the lives of the obese. Sexual, physical, and emotional abuse powerfully disrupts a child's Centers of Balance. Abused people are often very close to empty by the time they reach adulthood. They try to cover their hurt, shame, pain, and rage in a multitude of ways, often turning from one negative behavior to another. Food is frequently a favorite choice for abused people. They don't have to share it. They can be with this treasured friend, food, all alone where no one can bother them. Food doesn't hurt them in the moment and if they're lucky, there is an abundance of it. The emotional pain endures, but as long as there is food, there is temporary solace.

That is very often the case with people who are obese. A negative experience left them feeling badly about themselves. Food is used to medicate the pain but there is never enough food to make the pain go away. More pain is created from the problems caused by obesity. It is a vicious cycle.

An abuser causes damage to a child and then the child grows up and causes himself damage, often not having any idea why. If an abused child does not make the connection between his or her unhealthy adult behaviors and the painful events that happened in the past, that grown-up child will continue to eat too much or drink too much or smoke too much or shop too much or sleep with too many people or engage in a combination of unhealthy compulsive behaviors. Abuse comes in a variety of forms: physical, mental, emotional and sexual. (By the way, just for the record, spanking is hitting and hitting makes a child feel, well, hit. Being hit makes anyone, adult or child, feel hurt, anger and shame. Hitting a child spills her Cup.)

List any examples of abuse you may have experienced in your childhood (remember, this is your workbook – you do not have to share it with anyone; if you feel more comfortable, start a password protected journal on your computer if you want to ensure privacy):

_____

_____

_____

_____

_____

_____

Criticism: Abuse by another name

Overt abuse is hard to ignore. Criticism, on the other hand, can be subtle and easily ignored, yet the effects of criticism can be similarly harsh. Criticism comes in the direct, overt form: "What's the matter with you? You can't do anything right." "I don't know why I bother with you. You're not worth it." and the old favorite of the hard-core criticizer: "You're a loser."

Name-calling is also overt criticism: "Fatso," "Tub of Lard," and "Hog" are words that obese people know all too well.

But criticism can be even more painful when it's covert, or indirect. For example, if your sibling was not heavy and you were, covert criticism could come in the form of comparison: "If you were more like Susie, you'd have the opportunities to do the things she does, too." Or, everyone's favorite, "You have such a pretty face."

List any examples of being criticized you may have experienced in your childhood (think about family, coaches, teachers, friends, etc.):

_____

_____

_____

_____

_____

_____

Abuse by comparison

Often, comparisons can erode a person's self-esteem. Comparisons, too, can be direct or indirect. "Why couldn't you be more like your brother?" is the direct form. "I wonder how it might work if you tried to do the project the way Billy did?" is the subtle, but stinging form. A constant diet of comparison leads to inner turmoil, a lack of self-confidence, and anger toward the person to whom you are being compared. These feelings, if left unacknowledged or unexpressed, are directly related to overeating and other unhealthy behaviors in an attempt to "not feel." For a surgical weight loss patient, the consequences of repressing negative feelings are regaining weight, continued unpleasant feelings, and possibly switching to another unhealthy behavior.

List any examples of being compared you may have experienced in your childhood (think about family, coaches, teachers, friends, etc.):

_____

_____

_____

_____

Abuse by chaos

Brain imaging scans have now proven that the brain development of children who grow up in chaotic environments are different from the brain scans of children who are raised in calm environments. It is not surprising that children raised in calm environments have, overall, healthier and more efficient brains than children raised in homes where there is fighting or other forms of regular chaos.

List any examples of how your life was or is chaotic:

_____

_____

_____

_____

_____

Less Than Full is Less Than Full

Regardless of how a person ends up with misaligned Centers of Balance, it is imperative to find healthy ways to rebalance. When we feel incomplete, we turn to unhealthy means to fill the void. For bariatric patients, their primary means of doing so before weight loss surgery was food. After surgery, unless they seek to discover what voids their overeating was attempting to fill, they will either turn again to food and regain their weight, or they will find an alternative negative substance or behavior. For 30 percent of those people, that alternative is alcohol.

Abuse by another's addiction

Having a parent who is active in an addiction, whether to alcohol, drugs, shopping, gambling, sex, or food, creates a wellspring of negative emotions for a child, even when that child is an adult. Weight loss patients who are children of active addicts are at high risk for regaining weight or acting out in other negative ways until they deal with their own feelings about their parent's addiction.

List any examples of how another person's addiction may have impacted your childhood:

_____

_____

_____

_____

_____

_____

_____

_____

_____

_____

_____

_____

The Blame-Shame Game

Obesity is a symptom of underlying issues, a sort of nonverbal SOS. But who's to blame for the cause of the distress call?

I had a perfect childhood

The evaluation process before bariatric surgery involves the completion of a personality inventory. Nearly half of my clients complete the inventory in a "defensive" manner, attempting "favorable impression management." Obese people are sometimes unaware of, or guarded against, allowing themselves to acknowledge the problems in their lives and their buried emotional pain. This makes perfect sense. That's what they have used food to do: guard themselves from emotional pain.

Sometimes people insist that neither their parents nor their childhood experiences had anything to do with their being obese. In some cases this may be true. In most cases, childhood experiences play some part in a person becoming obese.

If you are going to be successful in managing your weight, filling your cup, becoming your authentic self, and finding and maintaining balance in your life, you've got to be willing to speak about both the good things that have happened in your life as well as the not-so-good things. You've gotta get real – with yourself!

A well-known saying in the world of recovery is, "You're only as sick as the secrets you keep." Now is the time to own any secrets you have been carrying with you for days, weeks, months or years. If you don't feel comfortable writing them on paper, then go somewhere and just say them out loud – even if it's to no one. If you want to, make an appointment with a minister, rabbi or counselor to talk about any secrets you have held in.

If you feel safe doing so, write down here any secrets you need to let go of in order to be your healthiest self (remember, you can write your responses on a password protected document on your computer if you prefer):

_____

_____

_____

_____

_____

_____

Sick and Tired of Being Sick and Tired

When you made the decision to have bariatric surgery, you were, as they say in Alcoholics Anonymous, "sick and tired of being sick and tired." You were sick of the way you felt. Tired of the fatigue that came from carrying excessive weight. Tired of the negative ways you were treated by others and sick of feeling the way you felt about yourself. You alone know the depth of the physical and emotional hell you experienced as an obese person. The decision to have bariatric surgery was a decision that you made over time, following failed attempts at weight loss in the past. Diet after diet, weight loss drug after weight loss drug. Hopes up, hopes dashed. Weight down, weight rebound. Finally, enough became enough.

You are finally on your way to a healthier life, a more balanced life, and a fuller life! In this chapter you may have identified some painful childhood memories. You may have realized some ways in which you continue to sabotage your environment, the primary area you have influence over in terms of your health and weight. Perhaps you admitted to yourself for the first time that your parents weren't perfect; your childhood wasn't perfect. (No one's is, by the way!)

It's important that you take some time from your busy world and let some of this sink in before you move on. Here are some ideas for "being" with the reality of your life.

What I Learned About Me

As you did the exercises in this chapter:

List (2) two (or more) things you hadn't thought about before that may have had a negative impact or your weight:

1. _____

2. _____

3. _____

List (2) two (or more) things you identified from your environment as a child that had a negative impact on your weight that you have continued in your adult life (NOTE: These are things we will work on changing!):

1. _____

2. _____

3. _____

ME...AS A CUP

Shade in how full you believe you are in terms of emotional health at this time in your life.

Shade in how full you would like to be in terms of your emotional health!

SLOW DOWN, YOU MOVE TOO FAST

(Do you remember that song? I can't help it – I often think in terms of songs and lyrics… I blame it on the Lovebug – my spouse – as he has played the drums his entire life and I have joined him in his habit of spontaneously bursting into song!) I digress… Most of us tend to move too fast – and too frequently. It's important to rest both our bodies and our minds at times. We've pretty much got the resting of the body built into our lives and yet even when our bodies are still – we keep our brains in overdrive… playing on our smart phones, watching television, and tuning in to our computer screens… all ways to divert our minds… from ourselves.

For seven days in a row, take a minimum of five minutes (please take at least 15) and sit and do nothing… no phones, computers, kids, friends, spouses or pets. Just you. Inside, outside, it doesn't matter. Just sit with yourself and the quiet. Think about the questions in this chapter. Think about your childhood, think about good memories, sad memories, healthy memories, unhealthy memories or whatever comes to your mind. Every day, for each of the seven days, write your reflections, what you become aware of, and especially the connections you make between your environment, any neglect or abuse, and your obesity.

Day 1 - Reflections about my life as they relate to my obesity

Day 2 - Reflections about my life as they relate to my obesity

_____
_____
_____
_____
_____
_____
_____
_____
_____
_____

Day 3 - Reflections about my life as they relate to my obesity

_____
_____
_____
_____
_____
_____
_____
_____
_____
_____

Day 4 - Reflections about my life as they relate to my obesity

_____

_____

_____

_____

_____

_____

_____

_____

_____

_____

_____

_____

Day 5 - Reflections about my life as they relate to my obesity

_____

_____

_____

_____

_____

_____

_____

_____

_____

_____

_____

_____

Day 6 - Reflections about my life as they relate to my obesity

_____

_____

_____

_____

_____

_____

_____

_____

_____

_____

_____

Day 7 - Reflections about my life as they relate to my obesity

_____

_____

_____

_____

_____

_____

_____

_____

_____

_____

_____

_____

Before moving on, take a day to reflect on your reflections! In other words, read over what you wrote for each of the past seven days. Write a paragraph about any themes that you discovered, things you hadn't thought about for a long time, feelings that surprised you, anything you might want to talk to a friend, relative, pastor or counselor about. If anything amusing surfaced, write about that, too. The process of working through this book can be a very serious one, but you are also free to laugh about anything silly that you discover or funny memories you have. Laugher IS great medicine – just be sure you're not using it as a way to avoid any painful feelings (leave it to a psychologist to add that…)!

What to do?

There are many things that contribute to a person's obesity: genetics, medications, illness, environment, history, and habits. Some things you have no influence over (such as your genetics, your past, and some illnesses). Some things you do have influence over (such as your present environment, the choice to deal with pain from the past, some treatments for various illnesses, and your habits such as food choices and whether or not you exercise).

The bottom line is: Regardless of the factors that resulted in your being obese, you are responsible for choosing what to do about it. You've made the decision to have weight loss surgery, which is a great start, but let's identify other things you have influence over in terms of losing your excess weight and keeping it off!

Influencing My Environment

List (5) five positive environmental changes you can, or have made since deciding to have WLS that make it easier to manage a healthier weight and lifestyle:

1. _____

2. _____

3. _____

4. _____

5. _____

Influencing My Pain from the Past

List (5) five positive things you can do to deal with any pain from your past in order to better resist food temptations as a way to avoid feelings:

1. _____

2. _____

3. _____

4. _____

5. _____

Influencing My Present Habits

List (5) five positive things you can do to influence your present eating and exercise habits:

1. _____

2. _____

3. _____

4. _____

5. _____

CHAPTER REFLECTIONS

Write down any thoughts you have related to anything in this chapter. What are the most salient points from the preceding pages that you would like to incorporate into your life? What thoughts do you have that you would like to discuss with a friend, therapist or mentor?

_____

_____

_____

_____

_____

_____

_____

_____

_____

" My Health. My Responsibility.
This Day. Every Day. "
Connie Stapleton, Ph.D.

God Help Me – Really
Your Spiritual Center

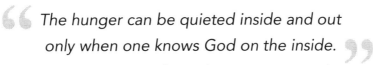

> *The hunger can be quieted inside and out*
> *only when one knows God on the inside.*
> **Author unknown**

As you already know, various factors account for obesity. Let's take a quick review of them now. Take a few minutes to complete the exercises along the way to help you get a more thorough understanding of the origins of your obesity. Our Spiritual Center is that core, the focus, the midpoint, the origin from which the other Centers stem. A person without a healthy Spiritual Center is incomplete. A person without a healthy spiritual center cannot fully nourish the cognitive, emotional, physical, social and enterprising centers.

Devoid of a healthy Spiritual Center, we become desperate, attempting to find the fulfillment that leads to a peaceful, harmonious existence within ourselves and with others through external sources. Our ability to be our authentic selves is clouded by self-focus and other-focus. The search is exhausting and futile. The only way to find joy and contentment and to live as the person we were intended to be is through a connection with our Creator. Obesity drastically interferes with the ability to remain in tune with God (or your higher power, a higher being, the power of love, or whatever manner in which you refer to your spirituality). Obesity inhibits our ability to nurture our relationship with God.

Most people who believe in God believe that we were created in His (or Her or Its) Image. Most people conceptualize the image of God as representing unconditional love, goodness, joy and beauty. If you believe that you were created in the image of God and therefore represent unconditional love, goodness, joy and beauty, there is no room for low self-esteem and abusive self-talk.

Without giving it much thought, list the first words that come to your mind which describe (5) five positive attributes you believe you were born with:

1. _____   4. _____

2. _____   5. _____

3. _____

Obesity separates us from God and from the person we were divinely intended to be. Our relationship with God is where our strength originates. People often get angry with, or blame God for abandoning them when the chips are down. The poem Footprints In The Sand, written by Mary Stevenson in 1936, provides perhaps the best answer to the question, "Where did you go, God, when I needed you?" The last line of the poem is, "The Lord replied, 'The times when you have seen only one set of footprints in the sand, is when I carried you.'" God carries us when the burdens in our life are too much for us. He helps us deal with devastation and loss. Think about when God has helped you through something that you did not think you could bear. It's likely you can think of several instances.

Spend a few minutes writing about one or two of the times when you felt the power of God help you through a period of time or a situation when you didn't feel you could handle things yourself:

_____

_____

_____

_____

_____

_____

_____

We need a daily, ongoing relationship with God to help us through difficult times. This includes needing God's help during difficult times related to food. Which means talking to God throughout the day: "Dear God, HELP ME! I crave something with a ton of sugar and know that if I eat it I will regret having done so. I know that with your help I can do this." Just talking to God will slow you down and give you time to remember that you have the ability to say no and help to make healthier choices than eating that "something" full of sugar.

You may need to make peace with God before you feel comfortable building or re-building your spiritual relationship. Are you angry with God because you have been burdened with being obese for part or all of your life? Are you upset because God could have removed this curse from your life and hasn't? Do you feel abandoned by God because you have asked for help to lose weight in the past but haven't been able to do so?

What has obesity cost you in terms of your relationship with God or your spirituality? As a way to begin working through any roadblocks to healthy spirituality, answer the following questions:

1. What has God and/or spirituality meant to you in the past?

_____

_____

_____

_____

2. Has God/spirituality played a major or minor role in your life?

_____

_____

_____

_____

3.   Have you blamed God at times for your inability to lose weight/stick with a diet/ follow through with exercise when the reality is that you are the one responsible for taking the appropriate actions to lose weight, stick with a diet and follow through with exercise? If so, what are some ways you can avoid blaming God (or anyone else) for the choices you make?

_____

_____

_____

_____

4. Take some time to write to God and let him/her know any thoughts and feelings you have about ways you may be upset, angry, disappointed in, or frustrated with God related to your weight loss journey and/or anything else that may be blocking your ability to have an open and trusting relationship with God. You can use the following sentence stems to write your responses, or you can take a piece of paper and simply write a letter, which you may choose to throw away after you have written and read it.

a. I am angry with God for the following things:

_____

_____

_____

_____

b. I blame God for the following things:

_____

_____

_____

_____

c. I feel I have let God and myself down in the following ways:

_____

_____

_____

_____

There are many ways to address any spiritual blockages you have. (If you have spiritual blockages, you can be certain they are interfering with your ability to sustain a healthy weight.) You can have a silent internal dialogue, write several letters and burn them so their message travels through the universe, or talk to a church leader such as a priest, minister or rabbi, or to a therapist. The point is to work through any hang-ups you are holding on to that prevent you from developing your Spiritual Center and finding balance there.

Balanced spirituality means you don't "hide" behind God or religion. It also means you don't spend all of your time at church, perhaps neglecting your children or spouse. Balanced spirituality implies having what people who follow 12-Step recovery programs refer to as "constant contact with God." Include God in your daily life through internal conversation, pleas for help, words of gratitude, and your interactions with everyone you encounter (especially your loved ones, as they are often the ones who get the worst of us, rather than the best of us, which is what they deserve)!

It's important to rebuild a connection with God to begin to find balance in your Spiritual Center. With a healthy, balanced Spiritual Center, you can nourish all aspects of your being.

List 5 to 10 ways you can increase your conscious contact with God on a daily basis, including ways to assist you in your efforts toward a healthier lifestyle:

1. _____

2. _____

3. _____

4. _____

5. _____

6. _____

7. _____

8. _____

9. _____

10. _____

Balancing Self-focus

Once you truly make God the center of your life through ongoing communication via dialogue, journaling, meditation or prayer, you need to work on balancing your relationship with yourself. Remember that you are a creation of God. The way you respect your body, mind and spirit reflects your respect toward God and yourself. Self-care is a way of thanking God for lovingly creating you.

Getting carried away with focusing on the self is an easy and common thing for obese people to do. Obese people are extremely self-focused. Be honest with yourself... When you are obese, you worry about what other people think of you, you wonder what they say about you, and you are hyper vigilant about people looking at you.

It's human for us to think about ourselves. The secret is balance: loving and caring for yourself in healthy ways and refraining from being overly self-focused in unhealthy ways. It's likely you have developed a habit of being overly self-focused as an obese person, but you may be unable to recognize the habit.

Write your thoughts about the following questions:

1. What are some examples of how, or when, I have avoided a person or situation because I was worried about what someone else might think about how I look/act/etc.?

_____

_____

_____

_____

_____

2. What are some examples of when I assumed others were looking at me or thinking negative things about me because of my weight?

_____

_____

_____

_____

_____

3. What are examples of other ways I was (overly) self-focused as a result of being obese?

_____

_____

_____

_____

_____

4. How do I see other obese people being overly self-focused and do I behave in similar ways?

_____

_____

_____

_____

_____

5. What are my thoughts related to the idea of being overly self-focused as an obese person now that I've given the idea some consideration?

_____

_____

_____

_____

_____

Taking time to exercise and caring that you look presentable in public are examples of a healthy self-focus. Missing your child's school play because you assume others will negatively judge your appearance is negative self-focus. Enjoying being the center of attention at a party for a few minutes can be fun, exciting, entertaining, and good for your ego; part of healthy self-focus. Creating a scene or being raucous at a party because you need to be the center of attention at all times is obnoxious and shines like a neon sign that says, "I feel badly about myself."

Consider how you can re-balance your self-focus. For example, rather than missing your daughter's violin solo because you don't want to be seen in public, remind yourself that her need for you to be at the concert is more important than your shame about the way you look. Instead of going out with the girls for the third time in a week, remind yourself that while your need to socialize with your friends is important, so is your family's need for time together.

It's possible and even probable that when you're busy assuming people are talking about you and/or having negative thoughts about you, they don't even have you on their radar! There's a "joke" that goes something like this:

When I was in my 20's, I worried what everyone thought about me...
When I was in my 40's, I didn't care what anybody thought about me...
When I was in my 60's, I realized no one was ever really thinking about me!

List (3) three rational statements you can say to yourself as a reminder that in reality most people are far less focused on you than you think they are:

1. _____

2. _____

3. _____

Preoccupation with self can persist following bariatric surgery. As you lose weight after surgery, it's normal to get caught up in the excitement of the changes taking place. The weight loss and accompanying activity is like a full time job! No wonder you become self-focused! Ask God to center you, to grant you discernment and balance, and to have a healthy self-focus.

Review the following list. Check any of the statements that apply to you:

_____ I've become so used to people commenting about my weight loss, that when they don't, I wonder why.

_____ I post pictures of myself on social networks on a regular basis, even though I didn't do so before I lost weight.

_____ Some people seem irritated or bothered on a regular basis when I share exciting news about my weight loss, smaller clothing size, non-scale victories.

_____ One or more people have verbally shared their frustration with me, noting that all I talk about since having weight loss surgery are the changes in my life.

_____ I weigh myself more than once a day.

_____ My significant other and/or children are complaining that I spend too much time away from home, away from them, and/or with my new friends since having WLS.

If you checked off several of these statements, it could be an indication that you are overly focused on self. Remember, it's balance we're seeking. Flipping from one end of a continuum to the other is not usually a good thing…it's simply a reversal of extremes. In this case, the extremes would be being overly self-focused in a critical sense on one hand, and being overly focused on the progress you've made in your weight loss after surgery on the other hand. Our loved ones often do not get the love and attention they need from us when we're too into ourselves.

List (4) four ways you were overly self-focused before you chose to have weight loss surgery:

1. _____

2. _____

3. _____

4. _____

List (4) four ways you have been overly self-focused since having weight loss surgery:

1. _____

2. _____

3. _____

4. _____

Obese people often don't have the energy to participate in physical activities with their children. They sometimes avoid social activities and therefore miss out on their loved ones' sporting activities, concerts or performances. They may opt out of social events with their spouse or significant other as well. On the other hand, as one loses weight, begins participating in social activities with new friends, starts enjoying shopping for new clothes, attending support group meetings and going to the gym, family members may still feel left out and not get enough of the affection and attention they need. Our immediate families and closest friends are blessings to us, just as we are to them. Maintaining balance in these relationships is an extension of a healthy spiritual center.

Write a paragraph describing the (5) five most important people in your life and the reasons they are important. How have you hurt or neglected these important people because of your obesity?

_____

_____

_____

_____

_____

_____

_____

_____

_____

_____

_____

List (4) four ways you plan to include these important people in your life and improve your relationships with them, as you continue to improve your health and balance your Spiritual Center.

1. _____

2. _____

3. _____

4. _____

Involving your loved ones in your process is a wonderful way to improve and maintain balance during this time of change in your life. Teach them about the Centers of Balance. Demonstrate for them the importance of having God at the center of your life so you can nurture the other areas. Have your kids help plan menus and grocery shop with you. Let them help pick out new clothes with you. Let them take turns being your "scribe" to maintain those food and exercise journals. Talk to them about nature and God's role in every part of our world. Be creative! Have some fun! This weight loss business can become too serious with all of the "shoulds, oughts, and musts" you are instructed to do!

List (5) five ways you will involve your loved ones in balancing your Spiritual Center during your process of change through weight loss:

1. _____

2. _____

3. _____

4. _____

5. _____

Letting Go and Letting God

The phrase "Let Go and Let God" is familiar to those in 12-Step recovery circles. As Mary Kupferle, author of **God Never Fails**, wrote:

"Accept the reality that God's wisdom is ever present and available, ready to fill you with new understanding, light and life. Let God fill every void, every emptiness that seems to separate you from the desires of your heart. Let go! Let God fill your need. …Whatever your life experience appears to be, you have, at this moment, an opportunity to let go of personal striving and let God move in you, and through you, to fill every need.

Tell yourself again and again: I let go. God will fill my need.

Let go. Let God fill your need. Let the creative process of God begin now to fill every point in your life that needs the touch of His great love and healing power. God is ready to do for you what you cannot do by yourself."

My "God Can"

Make a "God Can." Let your kids or grandkids help you or make one of their own! A "God Can" is just that… a can or jar or bottle that you decorate any way you'd like. Next to it, keep some blank paper strips or a cube of small pieces of paper. Use the paper every day – maybe several times a day – to write down things you can't manage/don't have "control" over (such as what other people think, the fact that there are donuts in the break room at work, how other people choose to behave, the weather, the number of fast food restaurants you pass every day, things happening around the world, etc.). After you write them down, drop the paper into your "God Can" and say out loud, or to yourself, "I can't do anything about this situation God, but you can, so I'm letting go of it and turning it over to you to deal with according to your will." Then let it go from your mind!

List (5) five things you can think of right away that you will write on paper and place into your "God Can":

1. _____

2. _____

3. _____

4. _____

5. _____

Building Balance

As you will notice throughout this workbook, I will be focusing a great deal on how you are thinking. The reason for this is because our thoughts are incredibly powerful and greatly influence our feelings as well as our behavior. Over the years, most of us have developed a firmly rooted negative self-talk vocabulary! If I could give everyone a gift when they have weight loss surgery, it would be the gift of removing all of their negative self-talk and replacing it with the spiritual gift of self-love and positive self-talk. Therefore, in each chapter of this workbook, you will have exercises specific to stopping the negative self-talk.

Read each of the following thoughts out loud, paying attention to what you are aware of in your body – how you feel when you read each statement and where you feel it in your body. For example, do you feel a knot in the pit of your stomach? Does your chest feel heavy? Do you feel muscles tighten? Are you sad? Scared? Angry? Then read the reframed statement and do the same – pay attention to how your body feels.

- God hasn't helped me out during all of the bad times I have had.

OR

- Sometimes it's hard to feel God's presence. I will make the choice right now to ask for His guidance, trusting He will provide it in the way He sees fit.

- God doesn't answer my prayers.

OR

- I will be patient, knowing God sees the bigger picture and believing He answers my prayers in the way that is ultimately best for me, even if I can't see it in the moment.

- I feel too guilty and ashamed to ask God for help because I stopped turning to Him for help a long time ago.

OR

- I can turn to God at any time knowing His love for me is much greater than I can understand. I will ask Him now to give me strength to make healthy choices today.

Write about what you were aware of as you read each statement. Did you feel a knot in the pit of your stomach? Did your chest feel heavy? Did you feel muscles tighten? Were you sad? Scared? Angry? Was there a difference in the way you felt when reading the first statement in the pair versus the second statement? What did you learn as you read these statements in terms of the use of negative statements versus more neutral statements?

_____

_____

_____

_____

_____

_____

_____

Write (3) three examples of negative thoughts you have related to God, to yourself, and to others that interfere with making healthy choices in your life. Then write a reframed statement that is more positive that will lead to making healthier choices.

1. Negative Thought: _____

_____

Reframed Thought: _____

_____

2. Negative Thought: _____

_____

Reframed Thought: _____

_____

3. Negative Thought: _____

_____

Reframed Thought: _____

_____

Throughout your day, when you become aware that you are making negative statements, make the active, conscious choice to reframe and restate your thought to something more positive. You will feel better and will ultimately choose positive behaviors.

Regaining Balance

Forgiveness is an essential part of Spirituality. Perhaps you need to forgive yourself for … maybe a number of things? Do you need to forgive yourself for being obese? For your negative self-talk over the years? For treating others less importantly than you wish you had? For giving up on yourself? For giving up on God?

Make a list of things you feel you need to forgive yourself for in order to be able to start fresh and to regain balance in your Spiritual Center:

1. _____

2. _____

3. _____

4. _____

5. _____

Write a letter of forgiveness to yourself:

_____

_____

_____

_____

_____

_____

_____

_____

_____

Your obesity has caused imbalance in your Spiritual Center. Regaining that balance will be a process that occurs over time. You will need to put forth consistent effort talking to God, asking for His help and for the help of your family and friends. It takes practice to "let go and let God." You have to learn to put your faith in God, trusting that He will give you strength to make the changes necessary to do the Gotta Do 'Ems so that you can take your weight off, keep it off, and work toward balance in all your Centers!

What role would you like for God/spirituality to play in your life in the present and in the future? Write a list of (3) three positive behaviors you will incorporate into your daily life to keep God at the center. For example: I will begin each day by reading a page from my favorite devotional book.

1. _____

2. _____

3. _____

List (3) three ways you will honor your Spiritual Center each day. For example: At the end of each day, I will remind myself of a God-given talent I have used in a positive way such as, "Today I used my gift of empathy to console my co-worker whose son is having marital problems."

1. _____

2. _____

3. _____

List (2) two ways you will ask others to help you keep your Spiritual Center balanced. For example: "I will ask my sister and best friend to gently inform me if they see me overextend myself/not set healthy boundaries by saying 'yes' to everything others request of me."

1. _____

2. _____

Once you begin to find balance in your Spiritual Center, you can start focusing even more on your thinking, on keeping an optimistic attitude and on maintaining positive thoughts, the subjects of the next chapter.

End of Chapter thoughts

Use this space to write down any thoughts you have about what you have read in this chapter or about the exercises you have completed. Maybe you don't believe in God and so this chapter frustrated you. Maybe you would like to deepen your relationship with your higher power. Maybe you are uncertain about anything related to spirituality. Take some time and let yourself write down whatever is true for you and how the information in this chapter sits with you.

_____

_____

_____

_____

_____

_____

_____

_____

_____

_____

_____

_____

_____

_____

_____

_____

_____

_____

I THINK I FEEL
Your Cognitive &
Emotional Centers

 *You must start with a positive attitude
or you will surely end without one.*
Carrie Latet

The following is taken directly from ***Eat It Up!*** (the book). I haven't changed it because, even if you have read the book, these thoughts warrant re-reading.

"Healthy eating and healthy living behaviors following bariatric surgery depend, in large part, on the balance of your Cognitive and Emotional Centers. These centers share a chapter because cognitions (thoughts) and feelings (emotions) are inextricably linked, and are closely followed by behavior. What you think affects how you feel. What you think and feel affects how you behave.

Clearly, the thoughts we have about any topic influence our feelings and in turn, our behaviors. Consider this domino effect:

Thought: "I think exercise is a waste of my valuable time."

Feeling: "I feel angry that my doctor and family members constantly lecture me about how I need to exercise."

Behavior: "I refuse to make time for something I hate."

Consider this alternative thought, feeling, behavior pattern:

Thought: "Exercise is really important to my overall health and well-being. Exercise is essential in order for me to keep my weight off following bariatric surgery."

Feeling: "I'm scared about exercising because it is new to me; yet, I'm excited about getting into it because of the benefits."

Behavior: "I exercise even when I don't feel like it because it is important for me in so many ways, especially since having bariatric surgery."

The thought-feeling-behavior pattern depends on you. You choose your thoughts!

Choosing Your Thoughts

Thoughts may "just pop into" our head, but when this happens, we then choose what we do with those thoughts. Here's an example of the domino effect of thoughts, feelings, and behavior:

Thought: "I couldn't count on my parents to be there for me. I can't count on my wife to be there for me. I can count on food to be there for me."

Feelings: Anger and loneliness because people did not provide him with comfort.

Behavior: Continued isolation and overeating leading to more anger, sadness and loneliness.

You can choose to alter your mind in positive ways, but you first need to learn to recognize what you currently do with your thoughts. If your thoughts are negative, you can dwell on them (if you want to feel badly.) You can opt to find a more positive way to frame the thoughts (thereby feeling better.) Your behavior will follow suit, depending on whether you focus on negative or positive thoughts.

As William James said, "The greatest discovery of my generation is that human beings can alter their lives by altering their attitudes of mind."
Changing the way you talk to yourself, think about yourself, and feel about yourself requires ongoing effort but doing these things does change how you think and feel about yourself, and ultimately, how you act.

Here's how you do it: As soon as you become aware that you are saying something negative to yourself, you think or say out loud, "Stop It!" Or imagine a huge, red STOP sign in your mind. Then change the thought as discussed earlier in the chapter. Say something more positive about yourself. Do this diligently, even when you feel too tired or defeated. Say something positive about yourself. Remember to talk to yourself as kindly as you would talk to your best friend.

Balancing the Cognitive and Emotional Centers

Balancing your Cognitive and Emotional Centers is a learned behavior. If you are an obese person, you have probably not learned to consciously choose how to think so that you feel and behave in healthy ways. Most of us consider our thoughts as unconscious. A mentor or therapist can help you learn the skills of paying attention to your thoughts and consciously choosing to focus on the positive aspects. These are essential skills for sustaining weight loss following bariatric surgery.

My Learned Thinking Patterns

1. Write a page (or more) about your parents' attitudes/ways of thinking. Was your mother/father the kind of person who looked on the bright side of things? Or did she/he tend to be cautious or scared or negative in her/his thinking? Did your father/mother encourage you to take risks? Did he/she talk positively or negatively about people and situations?

_____

_____

_____

_____

_____

_____

_____

_____

_____

_____

_____

_____

_____

_____

_____

_____

_____

_____

_____

_____

2. Write a paragraph describing how your thought patterns tend to be like your parents'; and how your thinking differs from theirs. Are you more or less critical than they were? More optimistic or pessimistic than they were? More or less self-focused than they were? Did they follow through on the things they said they would do? Do you? Did they encourage you and others? Do you encourage or discourage others?

_____

_____

_____

_____

_____

_____

3. What were you parents' thoughts about obese people? How did they make their thoughts about this known?

_____

_____

_____

_____

_____

4. What are your own thoughts about obese people in a general sense? How are your thoughts the same as, or different from, your parents?

_____

_____

_____

_____

_____

5. Write a paragraph about regarding how your learned and practiced thinking could impact your behavior, particularly as it relates to your weight loss and necessary behavior changes to manage your weight and your health?

_____

_____

_____

_____

_____

_____

_____

_____

Learning to be Judgmental

You are judgmental! Everyone is judgmental. Your thoughts and feelings about a person or a topic are your judgments about those things. We make "judgments" in order to make decisions. "Being judgmental" has negative connotations. To "be judgmental" in a negative sense happens when a person adds a value of "good or bad" to something.

The obese people I work with regularly talk about the frustration they feel when others judge them as being "lazy, irresponsible, stupid, ugly" or any other number of derogatory terms. Those terms, are indeed, laden with value ("good" or "bad") so name-calling of that sort is definitely "judgmental" in a negative sense.

Ironically, many obese people can behave in some extremely negative judgmental behavior themselves. However, their comments are geared toward other groups of people or other behaviors. "Why doesn't the alcoholic just not pick up that beer bottle?" "I can't believe anyone would ever even consider putting a tattoo on their body." These statements have a "value," of "bad" or "wrong" insinuated.

My Judgmental Thoughts

Write (3) three judgmental statements you make:

1. _____

2. _____

3. _____

Remember, no one likes being on the receiving end of negative judgments (including you, the reader). Most people easily identify when others are being judgmental but are unaware of their own judgmental comments and behavior (including you). Work on becoming more aware of when you make judgmental comments about other people. We don't know what has taken place in their life to contribute to their current choices or situations. And no one knows what sorts of efforts you have made to try to lose weight or what conditions added to your obesity.

Tragically, most obese persons judge themselves even more critically than anyone else possibly could. And it's not just in relation to their weight. For some reason, many obese people, even though they hate it so very much when others apply labels to them, do it to themselves! Maybe they don't refer to themselves as "lazy" or "irresponsible," or "worthless" but I've certainly heard lots of people call themselves "ugly" and "incapable of _____," and "hating my body," (both before and after weight loss), and "undesirable" and the list goes on and on. How much sense does this make? NONE!

My Description of ME

Make a list of your (10) ten best qualities, or things you like best about yourself:

1. _____

2. _____

3. _____

4. _____

5. _____

6. _____

7. _____

8. _____

9. _____

10. _____

Make a list of your (10) ten least-liked qualities, or things you like least about yourself:

1. _____

2. _____

3. _____

4. _____

5. _____

6. _____

7. _____

8. _____

9. _____

10. _____

Which list was easier? How do you typically describe yourself when talking to others? How about when you talk to yourself about yourself? Write your thoughts about these questions:

_____

_____

_____

_____

_____

_____

_____

_____

_____

Here's a challenge I pose to clients and am now presenting to you. I ask you, "Talk to yourself in only the way you would talk to your very best friend – even when giving them constructive feedback."

How I Talk to My Best Friend

Write a description of how you typically talk to your best friend, particularly if you are engaging in "constructive feedback."

_____

_____

_____

_____

REMEMBER: What you think affects how you feel. About yourself and every other thing!

What You Think Affects How You Feel and What You Do

Your Cognitive and Emotional Centers are not balanced when you regularly say negative things about yourself. Picture a child's teeter-totter with 20 negative statements loaded onto one side and no positive statements on the other side. In order to balance the teeter-totter, you must acknowledge positive things about yourself!

Imbalanced Cognitive and Emotional Centers usually tilt toward the negative. New ways of thinking need to be learned and practiced to improve your feelings about yourself and to achieve balance.

Feelings...Powerful Forces

Most people in the world have a limited awareness of their feelings. Sure, they know the words to describe feelings, but when it comes to being aware of what they feel in a given moment, they have a tough time. Most of us "think" our feelings rather than actually feeling them. We experience our feelings in our bodies, not in our minds. However, our minds are powerful in helping to create our feelings.

Many obese people actually use food to avoid feeling. Just like an alcoholic or shopping addict or gambler uses their substance or behavior to get away from negative thoughts and feelings... things they don't want to deal with. Focusing (thinking about) food, calories, recipes, what's for lunch, what's for dinner, cooking, baking, and watching the Food Network can occupy one's time and thoughts so thoroughly that it is easy to avoid negative or painful thoughts and feelings.

What I Avoid with the Use of Food

List (4) four situations you can think of when you "use" food as a way of avoiding a feeling or thoughts that are difficult or unpleasant for you:

1. _____

2. _____

3. _____

4. _____

Everyone deals with the four basic emotional categories every day: **sad, mad, glad** and **scared**. Learning to name (a mental task) and experience (actually feel the feeling in your body) how you feel is imperative in preventing weight regain. Unless you recognize, acknowledge, and then learn to deal with your feelings in healthy ways, you are at risk to use food as a means of avoiding feelings in danger of regaining some or all of the weight you lose following surgery.

Awareness is the name of the change game. By becoming aware of your thoughts and feelings you will be able to make healthier food and behavioral choices.

This may sound like a simple concept, but the reality is that most of us, when we actually feel something unpleasant, want to get away from feeling that way and we do things to accomplish that goal. Sometimes it's a good idea to put something "on the shelf" so to speak, as long as we address it later. For example, if I'm at work and I start thinking about and dwelling on an argument I am having with my sister, it would be wise to "put that on the shelf" until a later, more appropriate time to deal with it. If I continue to focus on it (notice I'm talking about if I continue to THINK about it), I am likely to feel more and more angry. I may then snap at my employees or co-workers because I'm in "a bad mood." On the other hand, if I make up my mind (again, a thinking process) to call my sister after work and to let it go until then, I can focus on my work tasks and choose to be grateful for my employees and co-workers. Having more positive thoughts leads to feeling better and treating others more positively.

Here's the deal, though! If I don't WANT to feel my feelings regarding my argument with my sister, or if I don't WANT to address the issue with her but I am angry about it on the inside, I will feel that anger in my body. My jaw may be tense. My muscles tight. My stomach may hurt. I might get a headache. All of these may be signs of not acknowledging my feelings and not dealing with them in a healthy way. FOOD can be the way people avoid feeling – experiencing the feelings in their body. If I eat, then I experience pleasure and can temporarily forget about the things that are bothering me. After time, we develop a habit of using food to avoid feelings.

AND YET, the feelings remain inside us. We need to deal with them in healthy ways (talking about it, writing about it, addressing the other person directly) or they build up and build up and we eat more or drink more or shop more or gamble more and develop unhealthy ways of NOT dealing with feelings.

The example of an argument with a sister is minor in comparison to some of the powerful and/or difficult emotions we experience. And many of the situations in which we use food to avoid feelings are out of our conscious awareness. Many are buried in our memories. The use of food may have started in childhood as a coping skill but is now a habit. For example, food may have helped prevent loneliness for a child. Food may have been a source of comfort from criticism, a reprieve from a chaotic environment, the single way of maintaining some semblance of control, or the one means of indulgence for a child. In adult life, however, the use of food as a coping mechanism will not ultimately meet the person's underlying emotional needs for companionship, understanding, or acceptance. For a child, food may be the best thing they could find at the time. Adults, on the other hand, have the ability to learn what their emotional needs are, to recognize that food will not meet these emotional needs, and to implement healthy coping skills and behaviors to meet their needs. Using food as an emotional pacifier in adult life does not lead to healthy, functional relationships or a healthy, functional life.

The Feelings Game

This exercise is to help you simply identify basic feelings. It's also a wonderful opportunity to involve your family as you learn and practice healthy new skills. AND an especially great way to teach kids how to identify feelings, learn what they actually feel like in their bodies, and develop healthy ways of working through their feelings.

MAD, SAD, GLAD, SCARED. Four basic feelings that each person experiences nearly every day. That's whey we'll start with these!

Every day, for the next seven days, complete these sentences:

DAY 1:

Today, I felt **mad (angry)** when _____

_____

What I did to deal with that **anger** was _____

_____

Today, I felt **sad** when _____

_____

What I did to deal with that **sadness** was _____

_____

Today, I felt **happy** when _____

_____

What I did to deal with that **happiness** was _____

_____

Today, I felt **scared** when _____

_____

What I did to deal with that **fear** was _____

_____

DAY 2:

Today, I felt **mad (angry)** when _____

_____

    What I did to deal with that **anger** was _____

    _____

Today, I felt **sad** when _____

_____

    What I did to deal with that **sadness** was _____

    _____

Today, I felt **happy** when _____

_____

    What I did to deal with that **happiness** was _____

    _____

Today, I felt **scared** when _____

_____

    What I did to deal with that **fear** was _____

    _____

DAY 3:

Today, I felt **mad (angry)** when _____

_____

    What I did to deal with that **anger** was _____

    _____

Today, I felt **sad** when _____

_____

    What I did to deal with that **sadness** was _____

    _____

Today, I felt **happy** when _____

_____

    What I did to deal with that **happiness** was _____

    _____

Today, I felt **scared** when _____

_____

    What I did to deal with that **fear** was _____

    _____

DAY 4:

Today, I felt **mad (angry)** when _____

_____

    What I did to deal with that **anger** was _____

    _____

Today, I felt **sad** when _____

_____

    What I did to deal with that **sadness** was _____

    _____

Today, I felt **happy** when _____

_____

    What I did to deal with that **happiness** was _____

    _____

Today, I felt **scared** when _____

_____

    What I did to deal with that **fear** was _____

    _____

DAY 5:

Today, I felt **mad (angry)** when _____

_____

   What I did to deal with that **anger** was _____

   _____

Today, I felt **sad** when _____

_____

   What I did to deal with that **sadness** was _____

   _____

Today, I felt **happy** when _____

_____

   What I did to deal with that **happiness** was _____

   _____

Today, I felt **scared** when _____

_____

   What I did to deal with that **fear** was _____

   _____

DAY 6:

Today, I felt **mad (angry)** when _____

_____

   What I did to deal with that **anger** was _____

   _____

Today, I felt **sad** when _____

_____

   What I did to deal with that **sadness** was _____

   _____

Today, I felt **happy** when _____

_____

What I did to deal with that **happiness** was _____

_____

Today, I felt **scared** when _____

_____

What I did to deal with that **fear** was _____

_____

DAY 7:

Today, I felt **mad (angry)** when _____

_____

What I did to deal with that **anger** was _____

_____

Today, I felt **sad** when _____

_____

What I did to deal with that **sadness** was _____

_____

Today, I felt **happy** when _____

_____

What I did to deal with that **happiness** was _____

_____

Today, I felt **scared** when _____

_____

What I did to deal with that **fear** was _____

_____

My Reflections on this Exercise:

_____

_____

_____

_____

_____

_____

_____

_____

_____

_____

_____

Make this a daily activity! It's great for a family activity at the dinner table or to practice when you tuck kids into bed at night!

VARIATION on this exercise: If you are a person who likes color, choose a color to represent each of the four feelings. Each time you do this exercise, draw something in that color to represent your feelings. This can help you get in touch with the feeling and you can learn what each different feeling feels like in your body!

The reason it's so important to learn to recognize what you feel is so you don't react to those feelings in harmful ways, such as overeating. Not only must you learn to stop and listen to what your thoughts are, you can help yourself learn to make healthy decisions by asking yourself what you need or want (emotionally) in the current circumstance.

Defense Mechanisms as Survival Tools

Defense mechanisms (which using food to avoid feelings is) help to protect a person from unpleasant emotions. Defense mechanisms, like childhood survival skills, are ineffective in healthy adult life, both in terms of overall health and in relationships. In order to balance the Cognitive and Emotional Centers, childhood survival tools and defense mechanisms must be recognized for what they are – ways to avoid current, painful realities. Healthy new coping skills must be learned and specific behaviors must be implemented in order for an obese person to lose weight and to keep it off permanently.

Defense mechanisms are unhealthy as they take rational thoughts hostage. They won't release the rational thoughts because, like a kidnapper, if they release the prisoner, they can't get what they want. People use defense mechanisms because they want to keep painful emotions at bay. If they give up the defense mechanisms of denial, rationalization, intellectualization, perfectionism, or isolation, reality and painful feelings creep up on them. Rather than facing reality and experiencing the feelings associated with whatever is going on in life, many people continue to use food, other harmful substances or behaviors to avoid any emotional pain.

A balanced Cognitive Center is dependent on dealing with reality. For the obese person, these realistic thoughts include some or all of the following statements:

* "I am an overeater."

* "I do not get enough physical exercise to balance the calories I consume."

* "I eat to avoid feeling lonely, hurt, angry, sadness, or fear."

* "I use food to drown my feelings of anger at my parents for things related to my past."

* "Food is my way to avoid my feelings of low self esteem."

* "My obesity is my main focus in life; therefore I don't think about other things that may be difficult to face about myself or my life."

Balanced, realistic thinking leads to balanced emotions. Knowing what you need emotionally leads to getting those needs met in healthy, appropriate ways rather than using food to avoid the feelings. For example: "I am an overeater. I eat to avoid feeling lonely. I am responsible to find ways to fill the loneliness in my life. Food cannot do that. But I can join singles' groups to deal with loneliness in a healthy way. I can also join a gym, a book club, and participate in numerous other activities. The choice and the responsibility are mine."

Knowing what you need emotionally can help you make good behavioral choices. If you take the time to discover what you need, you can choose a healthy way to get the need met before you react in an unhealthy manner.

Your thoughts are often subconscious, yet they still influence your feelings and behavior. Your thoughts are the key to understanding what your emotional wants and needs are in a given situation. Therefore, if you've ever wondered, "WHY DO I DO WHAT I DO?"... the answer is...You do what you do in an attempt to get an emotional need or want met.

Fulfilling Emotional Needs/Wants

For each of the statements below, even if they do not accurately describe you, write what the emotional need may be and options to get the need met in a healthy way:

1. "I do not get enough physical exercise to balance the calories I consume."

    a. The emotional need may be _____

    _____

    b. A healthy way to meet the emotional need would be _____

    _____

    _____

2. "I eat to avoid feeling lonely, hurt, angry, sadness, or fear."

    a. The emotional need may be _____

    _____

    b. A healthy way to meet the emotional need would be _____

    _____

    _____

3. "I use food to drown my feelings of anger at my parents for things related to my past."

    a. The emotional need may be _____

    _____

    b. A healthy way to meet the emotional need would be _____

    _____

    _____

4. "Food is my way to avoid my feelings of low self esteem."

   a. The emotional need may be _____

   _____

   b. A healthy way to meet the emotional need would be _____

   _____

   _____

5. "My obesity is my main focus in life; therefore I don't think about other things that may be difficult to face about myself or my life."

   a. The emotional need may be _____

   _____

   b. A healthy way to meet the emotional need would be _____

   _____

   _____

Acquiring the knowledge of new behavioral skills is only part of the solution. Some people say that knowledge is power, but knowledge by itself does not equal power. Knowledge put into action is truly powerful! Obtain knowledge of new skills, then use your new positive attitude and put the skills into action! The new skills? I'm talking about things such as journaling about your thoughts and feelings instead of going to the refrigerator, calling a friend instead of driving thru the fast food joint, getting on an Internet web site for bariatric patients, knitting, doing the laundry, visiting someone at a nursing home, rocking a sick baby at the hospital, planting a flower, cleaning a closet, doing a crossword puzzle, sending a care package to a friend, writing a long overdue thank you note, practicing the piano, washing a window or floorboard, going to a movie, reading a funny book, contacting a cousin you haven't spoken to in years, calling a friend and volunteering to babysit, going to the gym, staring at the ceiling…anything to divert your attention long enough to prevent you from engaging in unhealthy behavior. Who knows? You may even make someone else's day happier while improving your own.

Remember, insight into WHY you do or do not follow through with healthy behaviors is not what matters. Doing or not doing the healthy behaviors is what counts. Oh – and "TRYING"…"trying is dying," as they say. You either DO the healthy behaviors or you DO NOT. You either choose to eat a donut or you choose not to. You can't "try" not to eat a donut. You either choose to exercise on the treadmill or you choose not to. You can't "try" to exercise on a treadmill.

Every time you choose a healthy behavior you help balance your cognitive and emotional centers. You think about your options and you choose a positive behavior. This results in your feeling more positive, which in turn, leads to additional positive behaviors. Thoughts, feelings and behaviors…they're connected!

Head hunger

Head hunger can be as real as anything you may have physically felt before. However, "head hunger" is not physical. "Prior to my surgery, I was used to feeling really, really physically full before I stopped eating," Mark said. "If I didn't feel miserably stuffed after eating, I thought I was truly still hungry. Since having surgery, I sometimes long for that really full feeling. To me, this is head hunger." Kristy described head hunger as "the desire I sometimes have to eat, whether I feel physical hunger or not… it's about wanting food. The truth is, my head hunger is about wanting to feel satisfied. Usually I really crave emotional satisfaction, not food." Abigail said, "I had very bad eating habits before surgery. Now, at certain times of the day when I used to eat, I think I am hungry. To me, that's head hunger. It's really just bad habits. I had conditioned myself to associate eating with certain times of day, specific television shows, and when I did things like read."

To defeat head hunger, try one (or more) of the following:

* Talk directly to it: "Okay, here you are again, Head Hunger. Well, what do you want this time? Let me help you figure it out by asking myself some questions. What have I been thinking about? How am I feeling right now? What do I want or need emotionally? What is a healthy way for me to get that need met?"

* Using your own words, write down what you can say to head hunger the next time it wants to trick you into eating even though you're not hungry: _____

  _____

  _____

  _____

* Whether or not you are able to identify an emotional want or need, ask yourself: "What is a healthy behavioral choice I can make at this moment rather than choosing to eat?" Then DO that healthy thing!

List (5) five healthy behavior choices that you can act on rather than eating to support a healthy weight and lifestyle:

1. _____

2. _____

3. _____

4. _____

5. _____

- Tell yourself that even if you are physically hungry, you have planned to eat at a certain time, and until then, you will choose to drink water so there will be something in your stomach. Remind yourself that you can and will survive feeling hungry.

- On the other hand, you may be tempted to eat because the clock says it's time to eat but you aren't even hungry. One way to deal with this is to set an alarm on your watch or phone for three hours after you last ate and not allow yourself to eat anything until the alarm sounds. Other habitual times of eating may include while you're watching television, working on the computer, or reading. Being prepared with ideas to avoid habitual eating will help you prevent doing so.

List (3) three ways to prevent eating because you have a habit of doing so:

1. _____

2. _____

3. _____

- Head hunger can be triggered by commercials, candy dishes at the office, or billboards along the roadways. Making it a rule in your house to only eat in the kitchen (and to not watch tv in the kitchen) is one way to help. Having a glass of water or other zero calorie beverage with you at all times gives you the emotional satisfaction of ingesting something when you are faced with food cues.

List (3) three additional ways to prevent eating because you have been triggered by a food cue:

1. _____

2. _____

3. _____

- • Forbidden Foods? You need make some decisions about whether or not there are some foods that are not wise or safe for you to eat. For some people, the idea of a "forbidden food" simply makes them want to go seek it out immediately. For others, having "forbidden foods" is more of a safety net that prevents them from risking a possible binge or foregoing all healthy behaviors because one bite of a certain something means they have "blown it" so "why bother" any more? Some people can have a bite or two of a dessert or high carb dish and stop at that. Others cannot. If you are one of those who cannot stop or give up on all of your healthy behaviors if you eat even a bite of a certain food, then make yourself an "I CHOOSE NOT TO" list, a more productive name for a "Forbidden Foods."

List (3) three (or more) foods to put on your "I CHOOSE NOT TO" list. When tempted by one of them, remind yourself that you "CHOOSE NOT TO" eat this particular food any longer. Then feel proud of your decision and move on!

1. _____

2. _____

3. _____

_____

_____

_____

_____

Sit down and do nothing for 10 minutes. Nothing. Including thinking. Just breathe. Just BE.

The Committee in Your Head

We all have what's referred to as a "Committee in Your Head." Your committee members (all parts or yourself) chat with one another. You think about positive choices. You consider unhealthy choices. You waver. You disagree with yourself. Maybe you even argue with yourself. Argue away – just be sure 'the last word' you have with yourself is the one that chooses the healthy behavior or "the next right thing."

Maintaining Cognitive and Emotional balance are important when working toward the goals of sustained weight loss and balance in life. Food triggers act like rain hitting a sand castle to dissolve the foundation upon which our balance lies. Going to a buffet or reading cooking magazines can stir up the Committee in Your Head which awakens old negative thoughts. You know what happens to our feelings if negative thoughts take over. Negative behaviors follow negative thoughts and negative feelings. Therefore, it is essential that you minimize the triggers in your immediate environment and make choices to avoid people and places that have a potentially negative impact on your new healthy life. Cancel your subscription to all food magazines and get rid of all food channels. Stop pouring over cook books and recipes online. Tell your friends you don't go to buffets. Take your own food with you to social gatherings. Do whatever it takes to minimize temptation and to avoid triggers to negative eating behaviors. Bolster and maintain balance in your Cognitive and Emotional Centers.

Use the committee in your head to help you as you begin to use your thoughts to help you, rather than to harm you. Here is a simple step-by-step way to "talk to" your thoughts and determine if they are helping you maintain a healthy lifestyle:

1. Be aware of your thoughts, paying attention to when you are engaging in stinkin' thinkin', or thoughts that lead to your feeling upset in some way and thereby acting in an unhealthy way. AWARENESS IS THE FIRST STEP IN CHANGE.

   a. For example, if you think, "I can't exercise. I simply don't have time." If you are aware of that thought, then you can work to change it. (The word "can't" in this thought is a sign it may be stinkin' thinkin'.) That's why you need to work every day to pay attention to your thinking.

2. Ask yourself, "Is this true?" What's the evidence?

   a. What's the evidence that you don't have time to exercise? Is that a true statement? Write out your schedule? Is there time during the day when you watch television or play games on your computer or smart phone? (You could, then, make time to exercise – even if it's only short periods of time.)

3. Test the thought, if possible.

    a. Use the time you would normally watch a show you recorded or time you would play games or talk on the phone. Test it! You will probably be surprised that you engage in quite a bit of stinkin' thinkin' that isn't true - but provides you with excuses to forego healthy behaviors!

Thoughts, Feelings, Behavior

"The state of your life is nothing more than a reflection of your state of mind," said Dr. Wayne Dyer. A healthier body will result from your having a healthier mindset. It's true! As you tune out negative thoughts and practice choosing positive thoughts, your attitude will improve. Your more optimistic attitude will lead to healthy behavioral choices which will result in better physical health. Tell yourself, "Exercise is essential for sustained weight loss and better health. I don't always like to exercise but 'It's What I DO' and I love the way I feel afterward. I look forward to that feeling so I get out and walk every day. My cholesterol is at a healthy level and my blood pressure continues to decrease." Think about your physical health. As you do, remember that your thoughts and feelings about yourself, your health, and what you want for your life will lead to how you feel, to your food and exercise choices, and ultimately, overall physical and mental health. Your physical health is the focus of the next chapter.

CHAPTER REFLECTIONS

Write down any thoughts you have related to anything in this chapter. What are the most salient points from the preceding pages that you would like to incorporate into your life? What thoughts do you have that you would like to discuss with a friend, therapist or mentor?

_____

_____

_____

_____

_____

MOVE IT OR DON'T LOSE IT
Your Physical Center

> *" United States Dietary Guidelines, 2005: To sustain weight loss in adulthood, a person needs to exercise moderately to vigorously for 60 to 90 minutes daily. "*
> **Nutrition and Your Health**

Consider the list of activities that many people don't "like" to do, but do anyway:

- pay taxes
- brush their teeth twice a day
- write thank you notes
- do laundry
- go to work every day

Think for a minute about other things you do although you don't really "want" to.

Make a list of as many things you can think of that you do on a regular basis that you do because it's a (necessary) part of life! Even if some of them aren't literally "necessary," like writing thank you notes, a lot of people do such things because it's "the right thing" to do. What's on your list? And what is your motivation for doing this particular thing, the "why" you do it? For example, I brush my teeth twice a day. Why? Because I don't want to spend a lot of time or money at the dentist's office.

What I Do   **My Reason For Doing It; The "Why"**

_____   _____

_____   _____

_____   _____

_____   _____

What I Do	**My Reason For Doing It; The "Why"**
_____	_____
_____	_____
_____	_____

Use this list as a reminder that you do, indeed, engage in a number of tasks that, although you may not particularly want to do, you do them anyway! (As will be the case with exercise for most of you – if you want to keep your weight at a healthy level.)

Most of the people I talk to during their pre-surgical psychological evaluation tell me they are ready to do "ANYTHING, WHATEVER IT TAKES" to lose weight and keep it off. And then they hear what that entails (like exercise, eating very healthy foods, and not drinking with meals.) And they still say they are willing to do those things. And then they have surgery. And suddenly it's time to put into action what they professed they would do – NO MATTER WHAT – and things often times change. It's not that they didn't mean it when they said it, but the reality of exercising regularly, choosing the healthy food options regularly, and avoiding beverages with meals, after years of following well-established habits, makes it hard for people to follow through. But with consistent effort, the new behaviors can become the new, habitual way of doing things. And the benefits of doing so are plentiful.

Since this chapter focuses on your physical center, the discussion of regular exercise is going to be front and center. For some of you, just the idea of exercise wears you out, makes you sweat, and all of a sudden working overtime seems like a good alternative. However, you committed to a healthy lifestyle when you chose to have weight loss surgery. So, as a reminder to yourself, list (5) five benefits to you, specifically, that result from regular exercise:

1. _____

2. _____

3. _____

4. _____

5. _____

In addition to the benefits you listed, I have a few to add in case you didn't think of these. Obviously, you're aware that when you exercise you benefit physically. You see the results of your effort in decreased weight, increased muscle tone, the ability to wear smaller clothes, and seeing a more toned reflection in your mirror. Second, you benefit from a better attitude as your mindset and overall outlook improve with the increase in endorphins produced as you exercise (endorphins are your brain's natural painkillers that make you feel good). Third, you benefit from improved self-esteem, the result of looking and feeling better.

Be aware that there is a distinction between exercise and increased physical activity. And the distinction is an important one. You need to increase both exercise and physical activity following bariatric surgery.

Physical activity simply means movin' your groove thing. Getting your body in motion. Exercise, on the other hand, involves physical exertion, usually involving that nasty bodily function of sweating (I know you hate that), with the goal of burning calories and improving cardiovascular health.

Jot down some of the physical activities you do throughout your day:

1. _____

2. _____

3. _____

4. _____

5. _____

Exercising is moving your arms and legs, getting your heart rate up, sweating, and feeling the burn! Think melting away pounds, decreasing your blood pressure and cholesterol, extinguishing diabetes, wearing smaller sizes, and smiling when you look in the mirror! That's what you get when you exercise!

OK. Let's do something positive with any negative thoughts, feelings and memories you have in relation to exercise. You've probably got both negative habits and negative thoughts related to exercise. By working really, really hard to change your negative thoughts about exercise to positive ones, you're much more likely to change those bad exercise habits and create healthy, new exercise habits.

There's nothing creative or imaginative about this exercise, but it's the best way I know to help you learn to change your thinking… it's practicing and repeating, practicing and repeating and repeating and repeating and repeating some more. SO – I'll give you some negative thoughts that lots of people have shared with me. Your job is to find a way that fits your life to change the thought into a more optimistic one. The optimistic thought is more likely to result in positive action on your part. The thinking is one part… the doing is still… well, doing! Exercise requires action – movement – sweat! (You do many other things you don't necessarily want or like to do… read the list you made at the beginning of the chapter if you need a refresher!)

Negative Thought: "I hate to sweat."

Positive Thought: "Sweating means I'm improving my health, which is one of the primary reasons I had weight loss surgery."

Negative Thought: "Exercise is boring."

Positive Thought: _____

_____

Negative Thought: "I can't afford to go to the gym/purchase exercise gear and/or equipment."

Positive Thought: _____

_____

Negative thought: "I don't have time to exercise."

Positive Thought: _____

_____

Negative thought: "I don't see results fast enough."

Positive Thought: _____

_____

Negative thought: "I'm no good at sports or other forms of exercise."

Positive Thought: _____

_____

Negative thought: "I'm too tired to exercise."

Positive Thought: _____

_____

Negative thought: "I am embarrassed when I exercise."

Positive Thought: _____

_____

Negative thought: "I feel disgusted with myself because I don't exercise."

Positive Thought: _____

_____

GOOD WORK!

You have to exercise if you want to lose your weight and keep it off. I can't even pretend to sugarcoat this. There is no way around it. Now that we have established those facts, let's discuss what kind of exercise you want to do.

The choice is up to you, your sense of adventure, your creativity, and, of course, your current physical ability. Choose exercise that fits your personality.

Write down forms of exercise you enjoy (or might if you try it!)

Type of Exercise/Activity	Have Done It/ Already Do It	Wanna Try It
_____	_____	_____
_____	_____	_____
_____	_____	_____
_____	_____	_____
_____	_____	_____
_____	_____	_____

If you want to lose weight and keep it off, you must exercise. For the rest of your life. Period. In dealing with life after bariatric surgery, there can be no excuses. You must take personal responsibility for your choices and your actions. Choose to increase your physical activity. Choose to exercise regularly. Choose to enjoy it.

Sometimes people are great at exercising, but if their food choices are poor, their weight might not reflect the hard physical work and sweat! In addition to regular exercise, in order to have a balanced physical center, you need to eat healthy foods every single day!

You Are What You Eat

"You are what you eat" is not exactly a literal expression, but it's kind of funny to think about what the world would look like if that were true. If you looked like the thing you ate the most of, what would we see? If a person eats mostly foods that are high in fat, they are going to add additional fat to their body and will look fat. If they primarily eat foods that are lean, then they are going to look lean.

Let's do a little artwork! Use the following two pictures to help you see the difference in how your body looked before surgery (related to what and how you were eating) and how your smaller post-surgical body looks in comparison (again, based on what you are eating!)

In Diagram 1, write down the types of foods you ate in excess that contributed to your obesity before your surgery. If you want, draw a picture that depicts what this looked like on your body. In Diagram 2, write down the foods you eat regularly as a healthier post-op. Again, if you'd like, draw a picture of what that looks like on your body.

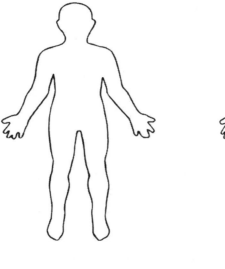 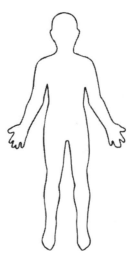

DIAGRAM 1   DIAGRAM 2

Use these diagrams when you want or need a reminder that what you eat does make a difference in how your body looks (and feels)! Makes a lot of sense. **How do you want to look?**

Doctor's Orders

Following your bariatric procedure, it is essential that you eat the types of foods in the portion sizes prescribed by your doctor.

POP QUIZ TIME!

1. Write down (5) five sources of high quality protein, which is what you need the most of (and be sure you're eating enough protein every day!)

    a. _____

    b. _____

    c. _____

    d. _____

    e. _____

2. Fill in the blank: If I return to eating the same foods I ate before I had weight loss surgery (even if I eat less of them), then I will _____ .

For the next (5) five questions, circle True or False.

3. It is extremely important that I take the vitamins I was told to take each and every day after surgery.   True   False

4. I take my vitamins and supplements every day (or as prescribed).   True   False

5. One of my goals for having WLS was to improve my physical health.   True   False

6. In order to maintain optimal physical health, I need to eat the way I was told to and take my vitamins and supplements every day (or as prescribed).   True   False

7. I am fully responsible for the choices I make about what to eat and whether or not to take my vitamins and supplements.   True   False

Taking care of your physical health leads to a balanced physical center. As with all of the centers, the physical center is interwoven with all the others. The care you take of your physical body impacts your body image, which is also part of your cognitive and emotional centers.

Body Image

The National Eating Disorders Association (NEDA) describes body image as how people see themselves when they look in the mirror or in their mind, what people believe about their own appearance, how they feel about their bodies, and how they sense and control their bodies as they move.

Let's see where you stand...Respond with the first thoughts that come to your mind:

1. When I look at myself in the mirror, I think _____

_____ .

2. When I look at myself in the mirror, I feel _____

_____ .

3. When I think about my body, what I say to myself is _____

_____ .

4. When I'm standing in public, I feel _____

_____ .

5. When I think of my heaviest friend, what I think about him/her is _____

_____

_____ .

The NEDA says that people with a negative body image have a distorted perception of their shape, feel ashamed, feel self-conscious, are anxious about their body, feel uncomfortable in their body, and are convinced that only other people are attractive. The organization also notes that people with negative body image have a greater likelihood of developing an eating disorder and are more likely to suffer from feelings of depression, isolation, low self-esteem, and to be obsessed with weight loss.

Who said I was...?

Make a list of any negative messages you got about yourself, your body, or your overall appearance throughout your life and note who said each thing.

Comment	Who said it	My age(s) at the time
"You're as large as a barge."	*My brother*	*Ages 10 – 15*

Repeat the following statement, referring to it frequently and using it to help improve your body image and overall self-image:

"I AM NOW AN ADULT. I AM NOW CAPABLE OF CHOOSING TO FOCUS ON THE BEST PARTS OF MYSELF AND TO LET GO OF NEGATIVE COMMENTS FROM OTHERS."

The NEDA describes persons with a positive body image as having a true perception of their natural shape and understanding that physical appearance says very little about character and value as a person. People with a positive body image do not spend an unreasonable amount of time worrying about food, weight, and calories. They feel comfortable and confident in their body.

Let's focus on the positive!

1. List (4) four features about your body that you are pleased with:

   a. _____

   b. _____

   c. _____

   d. _____

2. Write (4) four things you are grateful for that are physically easier for you since losing weight following surgery:

   a. _____

   b. _____

   c. _____

   d. _____

3. When I have negative thoughts about how I look, I can replace those thoughts with the following, more positive statements:

   a. _____

   b. _____

   c. _____

   d. _____

4. When I think of my best friend, what thoughts come to mind about him/her:

   a. _____

   b. _____

   c. _____

   d. _____

5. When you think of your best friend, do you think more about who she is as a person or what she looks like physically? What are your thoughts about this?

_____

_____

_____

_____

6. Get really brave! Call two or three of your best friends. Ask them the following question: "What are the first three things that come to your mind when you think of me?" Record their responses below:

a. _____

b. _____

c. _____

d. _____

f. _____

7. Based on the information your friends provided you in question #6, what are your thoughts regarding whether the people who love you most are more focused on who you are as a person or what you look like physically?

_____

_____

_____

_____

_____

8. I talk to myself as kindly to as I do when I talk to, or think about my best friend?   True   False

9. I am willing to work on thinking about and talking to myself about myself in as kind a way as I talk to, and think about my best friend.   True   False

10. The Challenge. Write a short paragraph describing yourself in terms of your value as a person – your body, mind and spirit.

_____

_____

_____

_____

_____

_____

_____

_____

_____

_____

_____

_____

_____

_____

_____

On its website, (www.NationalEatingDisorders.org) NEDA states: "We all may have our days when we feel awkward or uncomfortable in our bodies, but the key to developing positive body image is to recognize and respect our natural shape and learn to overpower those negative thoughts and feelings with positive, affirming, and accepting ones." That sounds like it could have come straight from the previous chapter, with its focus on replacing negative thoughts with positive thoughts, which leads to positive feelings and behaviors. Balancing your Cognitive, Emotional, and Physical Centers is hard work, but with practice, you can do this – if you choose to. Your health, physical and emotional, is, to a large degree, your responsibility!

A Letter To Myself

Write a letter to yourself telling yourself whatever you need to! You may want to apologize for being so hard on yourself. You may want to apologize for expecting so much of yourself. Perhaps you'll want to talk to yourself from your adult perspective to yourself as a child and remind the younger version of yourself that if others were cruel to you in any way that you are now going to protect yourself from being treated cruelly in the present. It might be a good idea to write to yourself about your character, which has nothing to do with the size or shape of your body. Remind yourself that the people who love you do so because of the qualities you possess. Most importantly, tell yourself you are going to make an effort to talk to yourself with respect, compassion, encouragement and appreciation.

_____

_____

_____

_____

_____

_____

_____

_____

_____

_____

_____

_____

_____

_____

Weighing In

"I weigh myself every day." "I never weigh myself; I judge my weight by how my clothes feel." "I get on the scale once a week." "Once a month." How often should you weigh yourself? This is a tough question because there is not one answer that fits all.

The purpose of weighing yourself should be to keep track of the direction in which your weight is going. After your body loses its excess weight and settles into a healthy weight for you, the reason to get on the scale is to see that you are staying at a fairly steady weight. For some people, that will mean weighing themselves daily or weekly. For others it may be every other week or monthly. Again, the purpose is to look for any major fluctuations or directional changes in weight.

I recommend that people keep a visual graph of their weight, beginning with their weight at the time of surgery. Then, every week or month, record the date and your weight on the graph. The first year to two years after surgery, the bar on the graph decreases rapidly as your weight decreases. After your weight has stabilized, the graph will remain fairly constant if you continue to maintain a balanced Physical Center. If, at some point, the number on the scale begins to increase and an upward pattern develops, you will know that you need to take a look at, and adjust your eating and exercise behaviors.

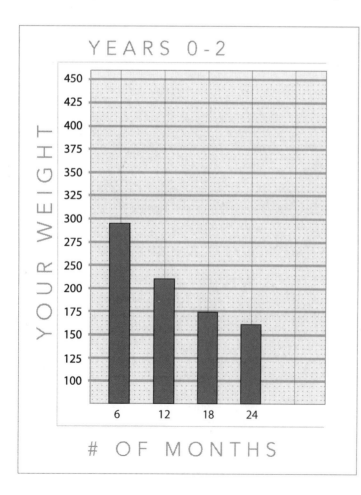

On the next 4 pages, use **Graph A** to chart your weight from your surgery date through the first two years following surgery. Use **Graph B** to chart the next two years; **Graph C** for the next two years, and **Graph D** for the next two years. This will give you a pictorial view of your weight for eight years. Using the graph, you can work to maintain a healthy weight.

Sample Graph

GRAPH A

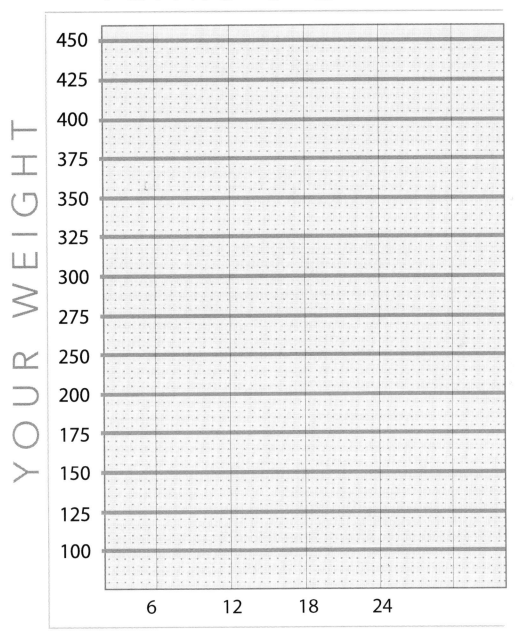

YEARS 0-2

YOUR WEIGHT

450
425
400
375
350
325
300
275
250
200
175
150
125
100

6   12   18   24

OF MONTHS

GRAPH B

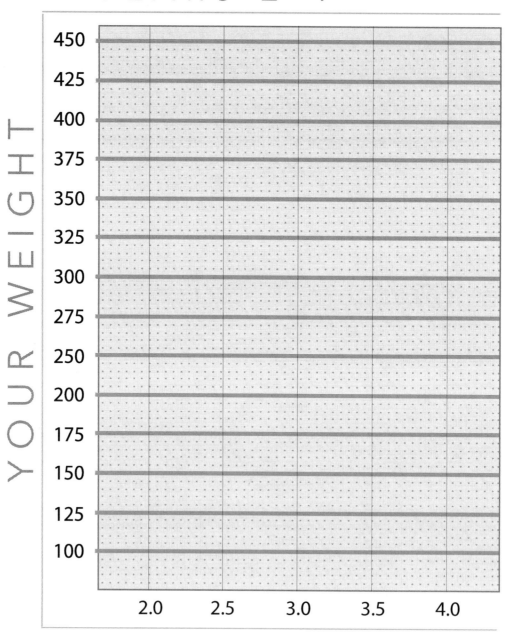

GRAPH C

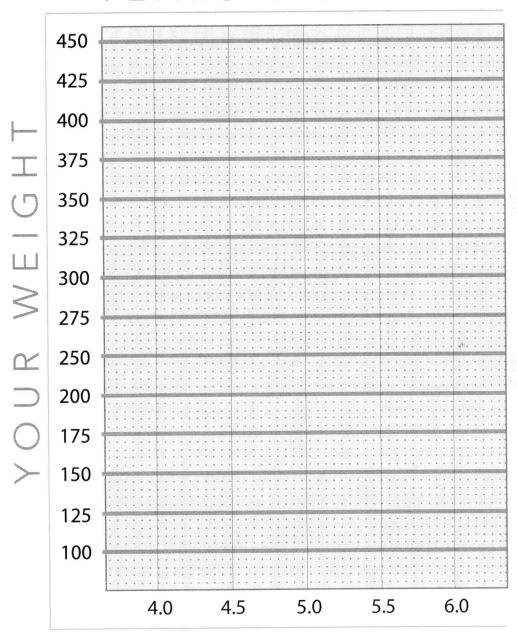

YEARS 4 - 6

YOUR WEIGHT

OF YEARS

GRAPH D

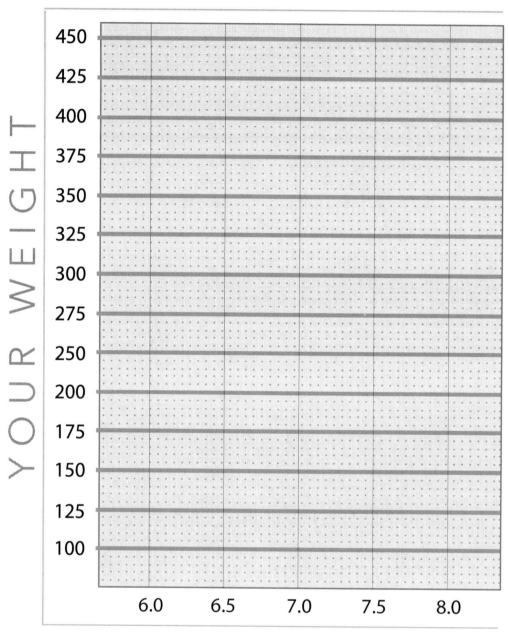

YEARS 6-8

YOUR WEIGHT

450
425
400
375
350
325
300
275
250
200
175
150
125
100

6.0   6.5   7.0   7.5   8.0

OF YEARS

Satisfying Head Hunger

Head hunger is often more of a problem for postsurgical weight-loss patients than physical hunger. Ann Capper, a registered dietician for FINDING Balance, a faith-based nonprofit organization dedicated to helping those who struggle with eating and body image issues, refers to various "false alarm signals that are often confused with stomach hunger." As Capper writes, "They are legitimate sensations, but not true stomach hunger." She describes a number of examples of what I call head hunger -- for example, "teeth hunger," when "we want to chew our frustrations away" or "mouth hunger," when "we see or smell something that looks so delicious that our mouths start to water [and] we desire to taste the food, but really aren't physically hungry." Capper also describes "mind hunger," when we eat because the clock says it's time to do so, and "heart hunger," when we eat to fill an emotional ache or void. Being bored and being tired can also stimulate us to eat.

These are great descriptions! It's worth taking some time to figure out if you sometimes mistake these forms of "head hunger" for physiological hunger.

Can you think of examples when you experience "teeth hunger," or want to "chew your frustrations away?"

_____

_____

_____

_____

_____

How about "mouth hunger?" Are there times when you "see or smell something that looks so delicious that your mouth starts to water [and] you desire to taste the food, but really aren't physically hungry."

_____

_____

_____

_____

_____

Do you experience "mind hunger," when you eat because the clock says it's time to do so?

_____

_____

_____

_____

_____

Are there times you feel "heart hunger," when you eat to fill an emotional ache or void?

_____

_____

_____

_____

What about when you're bored or tired? Are you tempted to eat at those times?

_____

_____

_____

_____

Whenever you feel hunger, it's a good idea to ask yourself, "What, besides food, do I want or need right now?" If you take some time and listen for the answer to that question, you may realize what you're really desiring is not food, but comfort, for example. Or maybe you're needing company but no one is available so you turn to food.

List some examples of times you eat but you're actually "hungering" for something emotional. Then list an optional, healthier alternative besides trying to eat your emotions away! You can always come back and add to this list as you become more and more aware of times you engage in this type of emotional eating.

Emotional need that I have eaten in response to	Healthy, alternative behavior
_____	_____
_____	_____
_____	_____
_____	_____

No One Can Do It For You...But You Can't Do It Alone

As always, you will need the support of others to help you when you are tempted to forego your exercise, when you want to make less-than-healthy food choices, and at times when it seems like food would fill an emotional void. Remember that it is your responsibility to let others know exactly how they can be of genuine help to you.

Make a list of those you can call on to help you retain balance in your Physical Center, noting specifically what you will tell them they can do in that regard:

Person	What you will tell them about how they can help you
Sister	*Remind me that M&Ms have never fixed sadness in my life (and they never will.)*
_____	_____
_____	_____
_____	_____
_____	_____
_____	_____

Your Physical Center encompasses more than what you put in your mouth and exercise. Just as with your Cognitive and Emotional Centers, establishing balance in your Physical Center highlights your need for the support of other people as you make the choices and changes that lead to sustained weight loss. A healthy, balanced Social Center is integral to achieve your goal of a full, balanced life following bariatric surgery.

" *The greatest wealth is health.*
Virgil

My Health. My Responsibility.
This Day. Every Day. "
Connie Stapleton, Ph.D.

Chapter 6

DO I KNOW YOU?
Your Social Center

> " *A healthy social life is found only, when in the mirror of each soul the whole community finds its reflection, and when in the whole community the virtue of each one is living.* "
> **Rudolf Steiner**

Every human being has a need to be "liked," "wanted," "desired," and to be a "friend." We are social creatures. We all want and need to be acknowledged and appreciated for who we are, for the good qualities we have, for the contributions we make, and for what we add to the lives of others.

Obesity can interfere with our self-worth. It can also negatively impact how willing we are to involve ourselves with others. Many people have an overt or covert fear of rejection. And sadly, obese people are sometimes rejected by others simply because of their weight. In each case, obesity can prevent people from enjoying the satisfaction of healthy social relationships with others.

The need to be social is ingrained and is a healthy, normal part of being human. For this reason, people will find ways to be involved with others. We tend to do whatever we need to do in order to be included. If we don't feel we are being accepted or don't believe we are acceptable, we can resort to getting our social needs in unhealthy ways. Or we may opt for social isolation.

Staying home when overweight is one end of the unbalanced Social Center spectrum. The other end of the spectrum is engaging in social behaviors that go against personal values (so as to feel included) or by spending too much time participating in social activities. A balanced Social Center lies somewhere in the middle: getting social needs met in healthy amounts and in healthy ways.

Initial Thoughts: *At my heaviest weight, did I tend more towards social isolation or social over-involvement? Did I maintain a healthy social balance in my life? Has my level of socialization changed since losing weight? If so, in what ways?*

_____

_____

_____

_____

_____

_____

_____

_____

Personal Boundaries and Your Social Life

People often discuss personal boundaries using the example of a fence. For example, a fence built around a house that has no gate for entry or exit is an example of boundaries that are too rigid. No one can enter or leave that yard. When a person is in a "fat phase" they are more likely to implement rigid boundaries. They stay home, spending as much time as possible there, interacting with as few people as possible. People who have boundaries that are too rigid fear (whether consciously or unconsciously) rejection. They isolate as a way to protect themselves emotionally and in some cases, to protect themselves physically.

Give examples of how I have demonstrated boundaries that were too rigid, whether they were specifically related to my obesity or not:

_____

_____

_____

_____

_____

Have there been any notable changes in my personal boundaries in this regard since I've lost weight? If so, in what way(s)?

_____

_____

_____

_____

_____

_____

_____

If there is no fence around a house, anyone is free to come and go from the property at will. Some people who are unhappy with themselves, whether this is weight related or not, will live without boundaries. They are often "used" by other people in a number of ways. Some examples include agreeing to do too many things: lead a scout troupe, head a committee for PTA, head up the office fund-raiser and be the treasurer for the church; over-committing in order to be included, to be approved of, to be "accepted," and to be needed. This leads to burnout and resentment. Not being able to say "no" is an example of having no personal boundaries. A person who agrees with the position of whatever group or person they are with at the moment also demonstrates a lack of healthy personal boundaries.

Another way people can be taken advantage of when they fail to set boundaries is sexually. In order to feel "desired" they engage in sexual activities with nearly anyone who acts as though they are interested.

Are there examples of how I have demonstrated a lack of healthy boundaries, whether or not specifically related to my obesity?

_____

_____

_____

_____

_____

_____

Have there been any notable changes in my personal boundaries in this regard since I've lost weight? If so, in what way(s)?

_____

_____

_____

_____

_____

A house that has a fence with a gate at the front and another at the back demonstrates healthy boundaries. People can come and go, but they must use the gates. As owner of the house, you can put locks on the gates at any time you choose. A healthy person, regardless of their weight, wants to have the equivalent of a fence with gates as their personal boundaries. They spend balanced amounts of time with friends, with family and by themselves.

Healthy Emotional Boundaries

Either end of a continuum is usually not the balanced, or healthy place to be. The truth is, few people, regardless of their weight, have been taught to set healthy boundaries. And most of us have no idea that we have poor personal boundaries!

When an obese person loses weight, they still have those emotional needs to be included, to be acknowledged, and to be liked. If they had the skill of setting healthy boundaries before weight loss surgery, they'll still have that ability. If they didn't know how to do it before surgery, they won't know how to do so after surgery. If they had unhealthy ways of getting their social needs met before losing weight, their ways of getting these needs met will sometimes take on a new look after weight loss. The newly thin person can still be taken advantage of unless they learn to set healthy boundaries. Losing weight does not have the benefit of automatically instilling these healthy behaviors!

It is common for people to swing from one end of the continuum to the other when a person alters their life in some dramatic way. People who isolated themselves when they were heavy may become socially overinvolved when they lose weight "to make up for lost time." People who had little interaction (and therefore little experience) with sexual relationships sometimes "go off the deep end" and partake in every sexual opportunity that comes their way.

Have I, according to myself or feedback I've gotten from others, gone overboard socially in some way(s) since losing weight? If so, how?

_____

_____

_____

_____

_____

Individuation

Individuation is the process of emotionally emancipating yourself from your parents--in other words, being able to say "No" to your parents without feeling guilty. Stated more simply – being able to set healthy boundaries with one's parents. I'll bet you think you have already individuated. I hope you have, although many people in their 40s, 50s and 60s have never accomplished this important developmental task. Try answering these questions:

* Are you in a job because your parents encouraged (or pressured) you to pursue it?

* Do you struggle at holidays, making sure you see everyone, so no one has hurt feelings - even though you are miserable trying to get everywhere in order to please everyone?

* Are you able to tell your parents "No" without feeling guilty? Without feeling guilty?

Individuating means being able to set healthy boundaries with parents and others. This is a difficult process because so many emotions are involved. Everyone, whether they are willing to admit it or not, wants acknowledgement, affirmation, and approval from their parents. People sometimes go to ridiculous lengths at their own expense to please their parents; these people are usually angry, resentful, and unbalanced.

Obese people often fail to set healthy boundaries with others in order to be included, liked, or approved of. Learning to set healthy boundaries is a process we develop over time. As you lose weight, you may need a jump-start course in setting boundaries (perhaps with the assistance of a therapist) in order to remain true to your goals of losing weight and becoming balanced.

The healthiest place to be in life, most of the time, is in the middle. Set boundaries based on your personal values. Learn to say "no" in order to remain true to yourself and the needs of your immediate family. Ask for the help of your most trusted friends, who have your best interests at heart in discerning what to do in situations where you're uncertain. Ask them for strength and encouragement to set health boundaries when it may be difficult for you (with family members, with "invitations" to participate in activities that make you feel special but may not be good for you, etc.) Bottom line? Always do the next right thing. Tips for balancing your Social Center are:

* balance time between your family, friends, and social obligations (this does not necessarily mean giving them all equal time)

* establish healthy boundaries for yourself in relation to others

* maintain personal values in your social interactions

* consider the needs and wants of others involved

Be prepared for personal and social relationships to change after you have weight loss surgery, and especially as you begin to implement healthier personal boundaries. You may feel guilty at first when you choose to say no when you're asked to do something you don't want to do, but ultimately, you will feel proud of yourself for taking care of your own needs.

Are there situations in which you know you have trouble setting healthy boundaries? If so, what are they?

Example: *"I have trouble telling my mother I choose not to eat the calorie-laden foods she continues to offer me, even though she knows I've had WLS."*

Example: *"I have trouble saying 'no' to men now that I've lost weight and have so much attention being paid to me. I feel bad about myself when I engage in behaviors against my personal values."*

_____

_____

_____

_____

_____

_____

_____

_____

_____

_____

_____

Alas, once again, no one can do this for you but you can't do it alone!

Who are the people in your life that will help you work through your boundary struggles? Make sure these people have your best interests at heart! What can you specifically ask them to do to help you?

Example: *"I will ask my sister to encourage me to say 'no' to mom as my sister has no problems in this area. I will ask her to role-play with me so I feel more confident when it comes time to setting those boundaries with mom."*

Person I will ask for help	What I will ask them to help me do

You may lose some friends in the process of learning to set healthy boundaries in your social world. When you start to say "no" to people and they aren't used to it, those who aren't your true friends may fall by the wayside. Let them go, remembering that you are worth having as a friend, even if you don't do things for others on their timetable.

Are there friendships in my life that have changed or are changing since I've lost weight? In what ways have these relationships changed? Are the changes due to my setting healthier boundaries in my life? Are there situations in which I have neglected some of my friends or family members since my weight loss? What thoughts and feelings do I have in regard to any of these changes? Are there things I want or need to do in relation to the changes with these people? Do I need the help of a close friend or professional to discuss the changes in my relationships, and my reactions to them? Do I need help in deciding how to proceed with some of these relationships?

_____

_____

_____

_____

_____

_____

_____

_____

_____

_____

_____

_____

_____

_____

Family members don't always like the changes you make in your social life when you lose weight, feel better physically, and want to get more involved in the world outside your front door. When friends, family members, children, and spouses say "You've changed" they also mean that your relationship with them has changed.

The people you love go through changes in response to the changes you make following weight loss. They too, experience new thoughts, feelings and behaviors in relation to your weight loss. Consider their feelings and their needs in this process. It is easy to become (or remain) overly self-focused as you lose weight and experience the world in different ways. Even though loved ones may be genuinely happy for you, they may also have emotional reactions they don't anticipate, such as:

* jealousy about the way people look at you after you have lost weight

* envy that they are not getting the same amount of attention as you

* anger because you participate in more social activities as a thin person and are leaving home more often

* fear (on the part of spouses or significant others) that you will become interested in someone else

* irritation as you learn to set healthy boundaries and start saying "no"

* annoyance at your seeming obsession with weight loss issues

* negativity and spite from family members and others for all of the above reasons

You may feel the need to be more socially active than you were before, or you may realize you don't need to be as socially involved as you were prior to losing weight. Either way, be sure to find ways to include your children, spouse, and other important people in your new activities. This will make them feel included in your new life. Finding balance in your life means considering the needs of others as well as your own.

In what ways can I include my family as my social needs and desires change throughout my weight loss process and as I become more physically able to participate in activities I couldn't before? (Remember, as you learn to set healthy boundaries inside and outside of your immediate family, you are teaching your loved ones to do the same!)

The changes that take place in your life socially may be confusing to you. At times you will be scared about people's reactions to your weight loss. The feelings you experience as people respond to you differently can be intoxicating. Or they can be infuriating. They can be intimidating and they can be exhilarating. Mad, sad, glad and scared. You'll feel them all in relation to your weight loss and the changes in your social life. Be sure to include the changes in your social life when you play the Feelings Game and give your family members permission to share their feelings (whether they are the same as yours or not) when it's their turn in the game! You may be thrilled about being invited to various social events but your kids may be sad and angry because you're gone more often! Support their feelings (feelings aren't right or wrong) and give them reassurance (backed by positive action) that they are the people in your life that matter the most!

Have there been times when I haven't understood the thoughts and feelings my family members have shared with me about my weight loss and/or the changes in my social life? Are there issues related to the changes in my social life that I need to talk with my partner, my children, close friends or other family members about? Do I need help from a trusted friend or professional to talk through these issues with?

_____

_____

_____

_____

_____

_____

_____

_____

_____

_____

_____

_____

_____

_____

MY SOCIAL LIFE: Pre- and Post- WLS

Complete the following form as a way of assessing your social calendar. Then answer the questions that follow.

Activity Pre- or Post-Surgery	Enjoy	Feel Obligated	Want Out	Hope to Start
_____	_____	_____	_____	_____
_____	_____	_____	_____	_____
_____	_____	_____	_____	_____
_____	_____	_____	_____	_____
_____	_____	_____	_____	_____
_____	_____	_____	_____	_____
_____	_____	_____	_____	_____
_____	_____	_____	_____	_____
_____	_____	_____	_____	_____
_____	_____	_____	_____	_____

To Tell or Not to Tell

There are a number of things to consider in determining whether or not to tell people about your bariatric surgery. The bottom line is that you only want to tell people who will support you throughout the process. An important issue surrounding whether you choose "To Tell or Not to Tell" is related to those good old boundaries we discussed earlier in the chapter. It is never a good idea to tell someone your whole life story – to include the issue of bariatric surgery – until you know them and can trust them. I always suggest to people that if someone tells you their entire life story within the first ten minutes of meeting you… run like crazy – in the opposite direction! Having healthy emotional boundaries means you disclose personal information sparingly to persons who have earned your trust. (Being a family member does not automatically guarantee trustworthiness.)

Your decision to have bariatric surgery is a personal one. Your decision to share the information is equally personal. Be smart. Choose to tell those persons you can count on to genuinely support you in the rough times and to celebrate with you as you achieve your personal goals!

A final thought: always consider your motive for telling people about your weight loss surgery. Motives can be healthy or unhealthy. Healthy motives for telling people would include: telling your co-workers in an effort to set boundaries in relation to their offering you unhealthy foods, telling your closest friends so they can support you in ways you specify, and telling all of your health care professionals – for obvious reasons. Unhealthy motives for telling people may include attempts to gain attention, attempts to obtain sympathy (trust me, it happens), or because your identity suddenly revolves around being a WLS post-op (yep – this too, happens).

Are there people I may need to consider telling about my weight loss surgery that I have been reluctant to tell up to this point? Have there been times I have told people about my weight loss surgery when there really wasn't a sound reason for doing so? Have I, in some way(s) had my identity become solely about being a WLS post-op? Have I gotten any feedback from family or friends that I talk too much about my weight loss, food intake, food in general, clothing sizes, the number on the scale, and other details about my life as it relates to weight loss surgery? Am I courageous enough to ask four or five people for their honest opinion as to whether or not I have done this? If not, why am I hesitant to ask them?

_____

_____

_____

_____

_____

_____

_____

_____

_____

_____

Communicating: The Hardest Easy Thing to Do

In our social relationships we communicate all the time. Verbally and nonverbally. Ineffective communication causes imbalance in our Social Centers because people misunderstand one another, fail to make their needs and wants known, and focus too much on another person's behavior. People retreat from one another when these things happen. Marriages fail and friendships end because of ineffective communication.

As long as so many things are changing for the positive in your world while you lose weight, you might as well improve your communication skills in the process. Doing so will help you deal effectively with your changing social relationships following weight loss.

Effective listening means paying attention to more than the words a person uses. When we speak to others we want them to hear both what we say and how we feel. When others speak to us, they want the same. When we let them know that we hear what they are saying and how they feel, they feel deeply understood. We all want that.
You'll be amazed at how much more productive conversations become, how much less arguing you do, and how much more you feel genuinely understood by others.

Sounds easy enough….but, as with most things, we need practice to get really good at something. Effective communication is no different. Another thing that's not so different about this… we usually think we're better at it than we are! AND we're usually pretty good about telling others how to do it even if we're not doing it ourselves!

We all hear things through a filter. If you were criticized a lot throughout your life, you are likely to hear even subtle, genuine feedback as criticism. For example, your spouse says, "It upsets me when you criticize yourself." You hear, "You'll never get better." Your sister says to you, "I'm happy you're doing so well with your weight loss, but I'd really love us to talk about other things more often, like we used to." You hear, "You think I'm selfish." In both cases, the receiver misread the intended message based on their own issues (which are usually rooted in low self-esteem and/or experiences in the past).

Listening Challenge: (5) Five times in the next week or two clarify with someone what you hear them saying to you. Simply say, *"I want to be sure I'm hearing you correctly. What I'm hearing you say is _____."* Ask them to tell you honestly if you heard them accurately and to let you know, if you didn't hear them accurately, ask them to clarify for you. Then ask them again if you understood them accurately. You may even tell a few close friends ahead of time that you are working on your communication skills and may ask them this question now and then. Below are places to record your five "practice" sessions. It will be a good idea for you to get a notebook (or start a "Communication Log" on your computer) and continue this exercise for quite a while. I guarantee you'll learn a lot about yourself – and other people!

Situation #1: What I thought I heard _____ tell me was.

I asked, and _____

_____

_____

What I learned from this is _____

_____

_____

Situation #2: What I thought I heard _____ tell me was.

I asked, and _____

_____

_____

What I learned from this is _____

_____

_____

Situation #3: What I thought I heard _____ tell me was.

I asked, and _____

_____

_____

What I learned from this is _____

_____

_____

Situation #4: What I thought I heard _____ tell me was.

I asked, and _____

_____

What I learned from this is _____

_____

_____

Situation #5: What I thought I heard _____ tell me was.

I asked, and _____

_____

_____

What I learned from this is _____

_____

_____

"I" Messages

The idea behind using "I" messages is to keep the focus on how "I" think, how "I" feel, and what "I" observe. We're all too adept at pointing out what "you" do (usually in a critical manner). People are much more likely to listen to you without getting defensive when you share your thoughts, feelings and observations using "I think/feel/observe."

Here are some examples of positive and negative uses of "I" messages. Pay attention to how you would feel if you received these messages:

Positive: "When you bring junk food into the house after you have agreed not to, I feel betrayed."

Negative: "You brought junk food home. You obviously don't care if I am successful at losing weight. I feel like you lied to me when you said you wouldn't bring junk food in the house." (NOTE: A feeling word should follow any time you say "I feel"… sad, mad, glad, etc. as in the positive statement above. Otherwise, you're not really sharing a feeling; you're sharing a thought.)

How would you feel if you were the receiver of this message? How would it feel different to you stated the two different ways? What makes the "positive" version of this message easier to hear as the receiver?

_____

_____

_____

_____

Positive: "I feel embarrassed when you make jokes about my surgery when we are out with our friends. I would appreciate if you would stop doing that."

Negative: "You embarrass me when we're with our friends. I think you're a jerk. You need to stop." (Note that "I think," was followed by "you" and a criticism; a misuse of "I" messages).

How would you feel if you were the receiver of this message? How would it feel different to you stated the two different ways? What makes the "positive" version of this message easier to hear as the receiver?

_____

_____

_____

_____

Positive: "When you ask me to drive to the majority of our outings, I feel taken advantage of. I would appreciate it if we took turns driving or shared the cost of gas."

Negative: "I'm sick of you taking advantage of me. You drive for a change."

How would you feel if you were the receiver of this message? How would it feel different to you stated the two different ways? What makes the "positive" version of this message easier to hear as the receiver?

_____

_____

_____

_____

_____

The point is to use "I" messages to focus on your own thoughts, your own feelings, and your own observations. Even if the person you're talking to doesn't respond well to what you say, you are making an effort to communicate in a positive way. And you are only responsible for your part, anyway!

Fair Fighting

If you do get into a disagreement with someone in your social circles, what makes for a fair fight? The basics for fair fighting include:

1. Talk about one issue at a time; the issue at hand.
2. Don't bring up past arguments.
3. Directly state what your concern is, using "I" language and include how you feel.
4. Avoid blaming, name-calling, personal attacks, sarcasm, and threats.
5. Take a timeout if you are getting too worked up; tell the person you need to take a break and resume the discussion in an agreed-upon amount of time.
6. Avoid the words "Why," "Never," and "Always."
7. Have your discussion in private; keeps kids and others out of it.
8. Allow both parties equal time.
9. Take responsibility for your part in the situation.
10. Accept apologies.

When emotions are intense, it can be difficult to fight fairly. Make the effort. The best way to keep fighting calm is to try to see the situation from the other person's perspective. This can be an extremely difficult thing to do, especially when we're in the middle of an emotional situation. We rarely hear one another when we're focused on defending our own position. It's very worth the effort, however, as arguments get resolved more quickly and with a greater sense of having been heard and understood by both parties.

Mind Reading

We want other people to be able to read our minds. They can't. It will never happen. You can't read theirs either. So "get over it" if you're one of those people who say anything even close to "Why do I have to tell him/her? He/she should just know!" People think in very different ways. You've gotta take responsibility for making your thoughts known.

Let's Practice! For each scenario below, write a sentence or two, using "I" messages to state how you feel and what you need using the following format:

When _____

I feel (or felt) _____

Because _____

I would appreciate _____ .

For example, your mother continues to offer you her homemade goodies every time you are at her house, even though she is aware that you have had surgery and you have attempted to ask her to stop this behavior in the past. You would say, *"Mom, when you continue to offer me the baked goods you make when I come to your house, I feel angry because I have asked you to refrain from doing so several times since I had weight loss surgery. I know you are a wonderful baker and are proud of what you create. I would very much appreciate if you would stop asking me if I want any and share your delicious baked goods with others. I don't mean to be ungrateful, but I need to take care of my health and if you can't stop, I won't be able to visit with you at your house."*

Now you try.

Scenario #1: Your spouse tells you they feel threatened by your weight loss and that they worry you may be interested in finding someone else now. (Answer this honestly if it pertains to you… feel free to skip it if it doesn't fit your life or answer it in case a friend asks you for help in a similar situation.)

You say, when _____

_____

I feel _____ because

_____

I would appreciate _____

_____

_____ .

Scenario #2: Your co-workers, who regularly compliment you on your weight loss, ask you to join them in going to the Chinese Buffet every Wednesday.

You say, when _____

_____

I feel _____ because

_____

I would appreciate _____

_____

_____ .

Scenario #3: Your brother-in-law makes comments about your weight loss over a period of months. You finally decide to tell him you had weight loss surgery. He says to you, "Oh, so you decided to take the easy way out?"

You say, when _____

_____

I feel _____ because

_____

I would appreciate _____

_____

_____ .

Scenario #4: A friend of many years tells you that you've changed since having weight loss surgery. She no longer feels like you have time for her now that you're going to the gym, support group and walking with your husband so often.

You say, when _____

_____

I feel _____ because

_____

I would appreciate _____

_____

_____ .

It takes courage and determination to say things you are thinking and feeling. It is hard to lay your thoughts and feelings on the table. It can be even more difficult to ask for help.

Learning to Ask for Help

A lot of people find it difficult to ask for help. Obese people are notorious for doing things for others. As we've seen, doing things for others can have the personal benefit of meeting one's need for acceptance or being included. Regardless, it is much easier for obese people to do things for others than it is for them to ask for help (except, maybe, at home, where spouses and children may become personal go-fers.)

What makes it difficult for you to ask for help? Underneath the reasons for not asking for help lie psychological insecurities. Pride? Arrogance? Insecurity? "I don't want to bother anyone" may really mean, "I don't think I'm important enough to bother with." "I was taught to do things for myself" might really mean, "I'm too proud to ask for help." The other end of the spectrum, of course, is asking others to do things you are capable of doing for yourself, even if it means having to push yourself more than you want to. When you were obese, perhaps it was easy to ask others to do things for you when it would have been good (psychologically and physically) for you to do it yourself.

Introspection Time! If I don't ask for help very often, what is that about for me? Am I ashamed to ask for help? Do I not want people to think I couldn't do something because I was obese? Did I not want people to think I was being lazy as that is a stigma often associated with obesity? On the other hand, do I ask people to do too much for me? Have I used "not being able to" as an excuse when the truth was I could have done some of those things for myself? Do I ask for help from others? What sorts of things do I allow myself to ask for help with?

_____

_____

_____

_____

_____

_____

_____

_____

_____

_____

_____

_____

_____

_____

_____

Learning to ask for help is essential for balancing your Social Center. Balance requires that you learn to give and to receive. Just like you enjoy helping others, they, too, like to be of service to you. Let them - when it's necessary and appropriate!

Incorporating Positive Thinking

Positive thinking is a critical part of improving balance in every area of life. The skill of increasing positive thoughts takes practice. (You know what that means...)! It's time to practice!

For each of the negative thought statements that follow, write down a more positive statement to replace it.

Negative statement: *"I get uncomfortable eating at restaurants because I think other people are watching to see what I eat."*

Positive statement: *"I can't control what other people think, feel or what they do. If I choose to eat in a restaurant, I'll mind my own business and hope other people do the same."*

Negative statement: *"My friend thinks I'm obsessed with my weight loss. She might be right but who does she think she is? Some sort of judge?"*

Positive statement: _____

_____ .

Negative statement: *"I don't care if people think I'm ignoring my kids because I'm finally being invited to go places with people and I deserve to do some fun things."*

Positive statement: _____

_____ .

Negative statement: *"Going to social gatherings is not something I want to do because no matter what size I am, I feel 'less than' other women/men and I end up feeling depressed rather than invigorated afterwards."*

Positive statement: _____

_____ .

Negative statement: *"It wears me out trying to be friends with people of the same sex. I'm always trying to think of the right thing to say. Developing relationships is too much work."*

Positive statement: _____

_____ .

Write (4) four negative statements that you tell yourself related to your social life and a more positive alternative.

1. **Negative statement:** _____

    _____

    Positive statement: _____

    _____

2. **Negative statement:** _____

    _____

    Positive statement: _____

    _____

3. **Negative statement:** _____

    _____

    Positive statement: _____

    _____

4. **Negative statement:** _____

    _____

    Positive statement: _____

    _____

Balancing the Social Center: Summary

A balanced Social Center requires being able to set healthy boundaries with other people. This is a skill that needs to be learned, along with practicing healthy communication. Sustaining your weight loss depends on your being able to set healthy social boundaries. If you are unable to do so; negative thoughts, negative feelings and unhealthy behaviors lead to self sabotage and often to weight regain as food is once again used as a balm to soothe these old patterns.

A balanced Social Center as part of a healthy lifestyle is essential for establishing and maintaining a balanced Enterprise Center. Your life legacy is encompassed in this self-actualizing Center, the focus of the next chapter.

WHEN I GROW UP
Your Enterprise Center

> ❝ *Happiness comes from spiritual wealth, not material wealth.*
> *Happiness comes from giving, not getting. If we try hard to bring*
> *happiness to others, we cannot stop it from coming to us also. To*
> *get joy, we must give it, and to keep joy, we must scatter it.* ❞
>
> **John Templeton**

When you were a child, if someone asked you, *"What do you want to be when you grow up?"* or *"What do you want to do when you grow up?"* what would you have said? Without thinking too much about it – what sorts of answers would you have given?

When you were a child, what did you want to be when you grew up?

_____

_____

_____

_____

_____.

Think back to yourself as a young person. What did you want your life to be like when you grew up? What sort of personal life did you want to have?

_____

_____

_____

_____

_____

_____

In addition to the kind of work you dreamed of doing, what else did you want for your life? How did you imagine your life would be when you became an adult?

_____

_____

_____

_____

_____

Our jobs, our hobbies, our community involvement, and the ways we choose to develop our minds make up our Enterprise Center. A balanced Enterprise Center leads to the fulfillment and joy of leaving a positive and meaningful legacy.

Just as it does with all the other centers, obesity causes imbalance in the Enterprise Center. Certainly, few people daydream of themselves being obese when they grow up. Being obese interferes with your hopes and dreams. Chances are, your life is different than you imagined it, specifically due to your obesity.

Off the top of your head, list specific ways in which your obesity has negatively impacted the dreams you had for your life. We will reflect more deeply on this throughout this chapter.

_____

_____

_____

_____

_____

_____

_____

_____

_____

Career

Has your obesity prevented you from living up to your professional abilities? Has your obesity restricted you from working in a career field you would love? How has your obesity caused imbalance in your Enterprise Center? To continue to determine this, answer the following questions.

Ask people you trust to give you their opinions about how your obesity has interfered with being involved in the above activities and include their responses when you answer the following:

* Am I working in my career field of choice?

* What would I love to do for a career?

* Where would my talents be best utilized?

* What kind of work would provide me with personal fulfillment?

* What prevents me from doing the kind of work I would love that would utilize my talents, interests, and abilities and provide me with a sense of personal fulfillment?

* Did I choose my career or did someone else choose it for me?

* If I am not doing work I enjoy, why? How has my obesity interfered in this?

* What would I need to do in order to work in a career field I would better enjoy?

Whether or not the essence of who you are (your personality, your character) is expressed through your work, it is important to find value in who you are more than in what you do. In other words, self worth does not depend on a particular title, just as how you feel about yourself does not have to be defined by the number on the scale. Regardless of your job title, or how much you weigh, you are you! You have a unique blend of personality traits, talents, abilities, ideas, sense of humor, and your very own experiences in life that makes you different from every other person who has ever lived.

How you choose to use this combination of traits and experiences is up to you. You may discover, as you think about these questions, that your parents or other significant people in your life have given you negative messages about what you were or were not capable of doing. Messages like this can be difficult to overcome but you do that by changing your thoughts, which we have discussed in previous chapters.

Let's practice now as it's imperative to let go of negative thoughts and feelings that may prevent you from the living the life you want to!

What messages, if any, did I receive about myself that may be negatively impacting my ability/willingness to pursue a job/career that I would be best-suited for/enjoy? Examples would be statements such as, "You'll never amount to anything," or "You're not college material," or "You WILL take over the family business because it's expected of you." If you received messages like this or other negative messages about what you could or could not do, write them below, followed by more positive self-talk you can remind yourself of when the old, automatic negative thoughts make their way into your brain and threaten to crowd out your hopes and dreams and determination.

1. **Negative statement:** _____

    _____

    Positive replacement: _____

    _____

2. **Negative statement:** _____

    _____

    Positive replacement: _____

    _____

3. **Negative statement:** _____

    _____

    Positive replacement: _____

    _____

4. **Negative statement:** _____

    _____

    Positive replacement: _____

    _____

5.   **Negative statement:** _____

_____

Positive replacement: _____

_____

Finances

Obesity can negatively affect finances in a number of ways. Think about the amount of money you have spent on diets, diet programs, diet food, doctor appointments, clothing purchased in a variety of sizes, and gym memberships that may or not have been used.

In what ways has my obesity negatively interfered in my finances? In addition to the examples noted above, are there other ways my obesity has taken a toll on my finances? Have I eaten at restaurants for most of my meals, resulting in spending more money on food than if I shopped at the grocery store? Do I make as much money as I am capable of making? What can I do to improve my financial circumstances? How has my health, in relation to my obesity, negatively impacted my financial circumstances? What are the areas of my health care that I can continue to work on to improve my health and therefore perhaps make it possible to improve my finances and/or my work/income opportunities?

_____

_____

_____

_____

_____

_____

_____

_____

_____

_____

Community

Being unable to volunteer as a coach for a child's sports team, to be a member of the church choir, or to participate in community theatre or join associations that have personal meaning to us… these are examples of ways obesity can negatively interfere in your participating in community events, either because of physical limitations or due to having shame related to one's size.

Do I actively participate in community/volunteer work? If I am unable to realize my dream job for various reasons, can I enjoy that type of activity through hobbies or community service? Do I support my community with active involvement in activities and events I enjoy? If not, are there reasons I don't? What sorts of activities would I like to be involved in? Where can I get more information about these activities? If I haven't thought of anything I would particularly enjoy, where can I find information about various options? How has my obesity interfered in my community involvement or lack thereof? What are three ways I can overcome my hesitation to participate in activities I would very much enjoy?

_____

_____

_____

_____

_____

_____

_____

_____

As a postsurgical bariatric patient who is successfully losing weight, you have surely gained valuable information from those post-ops who have gone before you. You will benefit equally by sharing your knowledge with others who are preparing for weight loss surgery and with those who have recently had their procedure. You understand what they are experiencing, both cognitively and emotionally. You can encourage them through the difficult times and celebrate with them as they meet milestones in their recovery from obesity.

What are some ways I help others and myself in the weight loss community? If I'm not already doing this, what are some ways I can?

_____

_____

_____

_____

_____

_____

_____

_____

Having balance in your life and helping others find balance in theirs is definitely a win-win situation. Use your talents, your wisdom, your creativity, your experiences, and your unique YOU-ness to contribute to the lives of others. This is how to balance your Enterprise Center and leave a positive legacy.

Hobbies

Photography, intramural sports, flying remote control planes, and hiking are a sampling of hobbies thousands of people engage in every day. Has your obesity interfered with your ability to pick up an old favorite hobby, or one you've always imagined yourself participating in?

Do I participate in healthy hobbies of my own interest? What hobbies or adventures do I dream about participating in during my lifetime? What things have I told my best friend I really want to do "some day?" Am I regularly improving my mind through continuing education, reading, watching educational television, etc.? Are there free/inexpensive classes I can take to increase my knowledge in areas of interest, whether electronic (cameras, computers, engines, etc.), educational (history, genealogy, medicine, nutrition, etc.), or purely fun (fashion, social media, geocaching, etc.)? Have I always wanted to play disc golf or try water skiing or hike mountain trails or be on a bowling league? How can I involve my family/loved ones in my interests? How has my obesity interfered in my participation in hobbies? What are the hobbies I will pursue in the next year?

_____

_____

_____

_____

_____

_____

_____

_____

_____

_____

Loved Ones

Spouses, children, extended family and friends are always negatively affected by a person's obesity. This can be difficult to come to terms with as no one likes to think of themselves as hurting the ones they love. Being unable (or unwilling) to attend kids or spouses events, needing your loved ones to assist you on a regular basis, and obesity-related health problems that cause our families concern are examples of ways obesity negatively affects our loved ones.

How has my obesity negatively affected my family and others I love? Am I involved in the lives of my children and loved ones, attending their concerts, sporting events, etc.? How has my obesity interfered in this? Do I show interest in the activities of my loved ones as a way to show my love, concern and support? If not, what can I do to engage more actively in this way? Do I owe anyone apologies for not being active or interested in their lives and activities in the past? If so, am I willing to make amends?

_____

_____

_____

_____

_____

_____

_____

_____

_____

_____

Happiness and The Pursuit Thereof

The Declaration of Independence says that people "are endowed by their Creator with certain inalienable rights; that among these are Life, Liberty and the pursuit of Happiness." Notice that the verbiage does not suggest a guarantee of happiness. We have a right to the pursuit of happiness. No one owes us happiness. We have the right to the pursuit of happiness.

"Happy" is what obese people often tell me they expect to feel when they have lost weight. Admit it … you've probably said it yourself. "When I'm thin, I'll be happy." In other words, thin equals happy. The myth that being thin equals being happy is simply wishful thinking. The dream of living as a completely confident healthy-weight person, a perfectly content new parent, or a blissfully happy newlywed is replaced by the reality that life is … just life. Fantasy is not reality. Thin does not equal happy. Thin you equals fat you minus excess weight: the same you with the same thoughts about self, the same childhood history, the same memories, the same insecurities, the same doubts, the same fears, the same strengths. The same you without excess pounds.

The healthier-weight you can definitely learn to be a happier you, but it won't be only because you have lost weight. Yes, losing weight can certainly give people reasons to celebrate as their health improves and they are able to have a better quality of life. Feeling better and being able to participate in activities with people you enjoy does increase moments of happiness. Developing positive self-esteem and appreciation of self are ways of increasing "happiness" on a more permanent basis. It is important to work on improving self-image, regardless of one's weight. This is a process that begins with how people think about and talk to themselves.

Write about how you may have, at some point in your life, thought being thin meant being happy. What have you found to be true about this? What have you found not to be true about this?

_____

_____

_____

_____

_____

_____

_____

_____

_____

_____

_____

"Happiness" is a feeling, a temporary state of being, a mood, a state of mind. Happy suggests euphoria or a heightened state of joy. Happiness is a feeling we experience in bursts. It is not realistic to expect to feel "happy" all day every day. Contentment is a more realistic goal. Contentment is being at peace with the way things are. For those of us fortunate not to be suffering from serious trauma, I want to point out that we create the majority of our own misery. If you and your loved ones are relatively healthy, have gainful employment and can provide for your family (even if money is tight), if you have a roof over your head and food on your table (even if your roof leaks and your grocery budget is limited), you have the essential ingredients for contentment. If you are discontent with your life, then ask yourself, "What keeps me from being content in my life?" Chances are the answer is, in one way or another, related to your attitude and your thoughts about your circumstances, including your weight.

Write the negative thoughts you sometimes get "stuck" on related to the circumstances of your life, which, if you focus on them, will definitely lead you to feel despair. Then write a statement that puts this situation in perspective and leads to your feeling better and having an attitude of gratitude for what you do have to be thankful for.

_____

_____

_____

_____

_____

_____

_____

_____

_____

_____

Response-ability

The author Stephen Covey notes that the word "responsibility" is the combination of the words "response" and "ability." Being responsible assumes being accountable. Responsible people are accountable for the choices they make and the thoughts they focus on. Your own sense of contentment is within your control. You are able to achieve contentment. Bottom line: You are responsible for your own level of contentment. Again I ask: **What stands in the way of your contentment? What are you doing to pursue your own contentment?**

My favorite self-help author John Friel, has discussed the difference between child-like thinking and adult-like thinking. Child-like thinking, of course, is often unrealistic, self-centered and based on a sense of entitlement. Adult thinking is realistic, rational and based on the fact that adults are responsible for putting forth effort in order to get desired outcomes.

Consider the chart below:

Child Thinking	Adult Thinking
I'm trapped.	I'm accountable.
I wait for others to make my life better	I have choices.
I wait for others to change	I find appropriate ways to meet my needs
I wait for others to give me what I deserve.	I take charge of what needs to happen.
	I can choose NOT to change, but then I don't blame others…OR…I choose to change.

As an obese person, how often have you felt "trapped?" Feeling trapped may have been verbalized as "There's nothing I can do" or "I've tried everything and nothing works." Write some ways you have thought you were trapped in relation to your obesity:

_____

_____

_____

_____

_____

_____

_____

As an obese person, have you waited for others to make your life better? Perhaps you expect people to wait on you in your home because you are too uncomfortable to do things yourself. Maybe you think it is your spouse's job or your child's job to make you happy? Have you said things like, "If my husband would get help for his anger problem, I'd be happier and then I could lose weight?" Have you thought, "If my family would stop bringing junk food in the house, I wouldn't be surrounded by tempting food, and I could lose weight"?

Write about ways you have waited for others to change, thinking you would work on your weight when they did something:

_____

_____

_____

_____

_____

As an obese person, do you wait for others to give you what you "deserve"? Do you think, "I deserve a raise. If I got a raise, I'd be a happier person"? Have you complained, "People treat obese people badly. I deserve to be treated better by others. I'd be a more pleasant person if people were nicer to me"?

Write about ways you have waited for others to "give you what you deserve":

_____

_____

_____

_____

_____

Adult thinking would go like this: *"I'm not trapped by my obesity. The time has come for me to take responsibility for my health. I am accountable for making the changes in my eating and exercise habits, and I choose to begin today. I have choices as to how I want to go about losing weight. I need to find ways to meet my own needs."*

Everyone, large or small, red, black or white, blonde or brunette, "deserves" the same things. No one is more deserving than another of anything. Please be "mindful" of saying you "deserve" this or that, at least if you think you are in some way, more deserving of it than another person.

Obesity, Contentment, Response-ability

Let's look at the idea of "response abilities" and "account abilities" more closely. If you are obese, and if you do not want to remain obese, you are responsible and able to choose your responses (make the changes) in your life that will result in your no longer being obese. Having bariatric surgery is a responsible choice toward achieving your goal of better health and increased satisfaction with life.

Write about how you are currently taking responsibility for your recovery from obesity:

_____

_____

_____

_____

_____

_____

_____

How are you finding appropriate ways to get your needs met?

_____

_____

_____

_____

_____

_____

_____

_____

Choosing to make your life happier, more content, and more balanced in several arenas results in helping to balance your Enterprise Center. To attain this balance, you must take personal responsibility for the following:

- Choose to address your family history and work on issues that have contributed to your obesity and imbalance in your Enterprise Center.

- Choose to make your spiritual life the center of your world in order to find balance in your Enterprise Center.

- Choose what messages you were given about yourself that you want to keep and which you want to change; then get help in learning to change them.

- Choose what parenting techniques you learned from your parents that you want to keep and which you want to change; then get help in learning healthy parenting techniques.

- Choose what communication techniques you have learned that you want to get rid of (sarcasm, criticism) and get help in learning effective communication tools.

- Choose to set healthy boundaries with others; get help in learning how to set boundaries.

- Choose to set realistic, measurable goals and find ways to meet them, asking for help.

- Choose to implement physical activity and exercise into your life; then do it!

- Choose to learn and utilize positive thinking in your life and practice it daily.

- Choose to focus on gratitude in your life.

- Choose to have a healthy and balanced social life.

- Choose to work diligently to maintain balance in your life.

- Choose to complete the Gotta Do Ems daily!

A balanced Enterprise Center requires you to take personal responsibility for your choices and behaviors, especially your choices and behaviors related to eating and physical activity. Regardless of what happened in your childhood, regardless of what your current circumstances are, if you want to lose weight and keep it off, you are responsible for engaging in the behaviors necessary to do so.

Losing weight and keeping it off does not "just happen." No one can do the work for you. Commitment and perseverance are necessary. Commitment and perseverance are choices you must make on a daily basis.

As you gain a new sense of self by continuing to make choices that lead toward healthy living, you may also discover that you are able to make choices that bring your Enterprise Center back into balance.

Write about the following:

Steven Covey suggests, "How I want a) my children, b) my spouse, c) a co-worker, and d) a friend to describe me is: _____

_____

_____

_____

_____

At the end of every day, ask yourself, "Today - have I lived up to the description of how I want others to describe me?" _____

_____

_____

_____

_____

With the power gained from making healthy choices and implementing the thought processes and behaviors necessary to lose weight and keep it off, you may find that you are able to pursue the dreams and aspirations you thought impossible as an obese person. Making healthy choices and staying true to them can be like travelling along a tough road, one that comparatively few people are able to follow. The final chapter of this book invites you to walk that road – the road too infrequently chosen.

Chapter 8

THE ROAD INFREQUENTLY TRAVELED
Centers of Balance & Sustained Weight Loss

The natural and logical consequence of completing the **Gotta Do Ems** on a daily basis is sustained weight loss and a full, healthy life. Those who lose their weight following surgery and keep it off do the things *necessary* to keep their weight off. These are the people who take the road not so frequently travelled, as evidenced by the fact that so many people do regain a substantial amount of weight, whether they get help to lose it through surgical means or otherwise. In order to be on this esteemed road to sustained weight loss, you've gotta make consistently healthy food choices, maintain portion control, exercise regularly, drink water throughout the day, eat breakfast, plan your meals and follow your plan, keep food and exercise journals, get plenty of sleep, utilize a healthy support system and, if necessary, participate in individual and/or group counseling. To keep your weight off, complete the **Gotta Do Ems!**

The road infrequently traveled leads to sustained weight loss and balance in life. This road is infrequently traveled because "it's hard."

What are some ways you have avoided following the **Gotta Do Ems** in the past because they felt "hard?"

_____

_____

_____

_____

_____

_____

_____

_____

_____

To stay on this road of sustained weight loss requires a consistent determination to maintain a positive attitude, the perseverance to complete the GDEs on a daily basis, the courage to reach out and ask for help from others, the willingness to look at potentially painful emotional issues underlying obesity and a commitment to be your best self, the authentic person God placed you on this earth to grow into – before other people and the world had a chance to interfere. The road infrequently traveled leads to wonderful places: a life with good physical and emotional health, balanced Centers, and to living Contentedly-Ever-After.

STOP Dieting

I have yet to meet a person preparing for bariatric surgery who has not gone on (and off) innumerable diets. The results are uniformly the same. "I lost weight until I went off the diet. Then I gained back all of the weight I lost plus some." Newsflash: Diets don't work.

List the "diets" you have gone on SINCE having weight loss surgery:

_____

_____

_____

_____

_____

_____

Diets don't "work" for the following reasons:

- The goal of a diet is to lose weight, but the real goal is to keep the weight off. Diets only address losing weight.

- Many diets require people to eat pre-packaged food specific to that diet, exist on a liquid diet, follow a prescribed menu for a certain number of weeks, or reduce or eliminate an entire category of food. These "diets" won't work unless you are willing to do one of two things: 1) continue to eat the pre-packaged diet food, exist on a liquid diet, follow a prescribed menu, or reduce or eliminate an entire category of food for the rest of your life, or 2) eat healthy, balanced meals consisting of real food and refrain from "picking up where you left off" before the diet for the rest of your life.

- The diet may rely on diet pills. As soon as you quit taking diet pills, if you don't make the lifestyle changes required to stay at a healthy weight, you will gain your weight back.

- The diet may require consuming a very low number of calories. Any diet that results in significant weight loss is essentially a very low calorie diet. Add up the calories of one day's worth of the pre-packed diet food or the liquid "meals" or the prescribed food plans. What you will discover is that the total caloric intake is most likely less than 1200 calories per day. The pouch created by your weight loss procedure will ensure a fairly low amount of calories IF you make healthy food choices (like you agreed to before surgery).

So STOP dieting! Dieting may have become a bad habit in your life. The goal is to eventually incorporate the healthy new habits after weight loss surgery so that they become a way of life. If you live by the Gotta Do Ems, you won't have a need to "diet."

I rarely have concerns about people losing their excess weight after surgery. Most do. I have tremendous concern about people not realizing that they can put their weight back on following the surgery. And many people do regain weight. People who gain their weight back often say things like, "The surgery didn't work." That's because the surgery doesn't work! YOU either work or YOU don't. Remember, as they say in AA, "If you always do what you always did, you'll always get what you always got." In other words, if you were obese because you ate too much of the wrong things and didn't exercise before your surgery, you will be obese if you return to overeating the wrong things and not exercising after your surgery.

Gotta Do Ems Along the Road

Let's review the **Gotta Do Ems** for Sustained Weight Loss Success one at a time. Make up your mind that you are going to take the Road Infrequently Traveled every day – one day at a time. By doing so, you'll be one of the people who get the Results Too-Infrequently Obtained: sustained weight loss, improved health, and balanced Centers for a Lifetime!

The Gotta Do Ems for Sustained Weight Loss Success

1. **Make consistently healthy food choices (protein first)**
   Your body, after surgery, will obtain all of its nutrition from the food you put into your egg-sized pouch three to five times a day. Because that small amount of food needs to provide your body with all of the nutrients it needs to remain healthy, your food choices need to be made exceptionally carefully. Your body needs up to 60 grams of protein every day after you have had a bariatric procedure. That's a lot of protein! Very rarely do you want to put anything in your mouth (solid or liquid) that doesn't contain nutritional value. And if you want the rewards of taking that Road Infrequently Traveled, you need to eat this way every single day.

   Here's a reminder of a list of foods with good quality protein.

Food	Quantity	Protein Grams
Egg	1 Medium	6
Milk (Skim)	1 Cup	8
Soy Milk	1 Cup	6-10
Cottage Cheese (2%)	1/2 Cup	16
Cheddar Cheese	1 Ounce	7
Mozarella, Part Skim	1 Ounce	8
Ricotta Cheese, Part Skim	1/2 Cup	10
Yogurt, Low-Fat, Plain	1 Cup	12
Roast Chicken	4 Ounces	31
Ground Beef, Extra Lean	4 Ounces	33
Sirloin Steak, Choice Cut, Trimmed	4 Ounces	35
Tuna, Canned in Water	4 Ounces	33
Most fish fillets	3.5 Ounces	22
Turkey Breast, Roasted no skin	4 Ounces	35
Roast Beef	3.5 Ounces	28

Food	Quantity	Protein Grams
Pork loin or tenerloin	4 Ounces	29
Bacon	1 Slice	3
Ham	3.5 Ounces	18
Oatmeal (Cooked)	1 Cup	6
Rice, Brown (Cooked)	1 Cup	5
Spaghetti (Cooked)	1 Cup	6
Whole Wheat Bread	2 Slices	6
Almonds	1 Ounce	6
Cashews, Dry Roasted	1 ounce	4
Peanuts	1/4 Cup	9
Pecans	1/4 Cup	2.5
Sunflower Seeds	1/4 Cup	6
Flax Seeds	1/4 Cup	6
Lentils (Cooked)	1/2 Cup	8
Lima Beans (Cooked)	1/2 Cup	8
Peanut Butter	2 Tbsp	10
Red Kidney Beans (Canned)	1/2 Cup	8
Soybeans (Cooked)	1/2 Cup	10
Tofu	4 Ounces	9

From this list, my (10) ten favorites, which I will be sure to have at home and work and (at least one) in my purse or briefcase at all times are:

1. _____   6. _____

2. _____   7. _____

3. _____   8. _____

4. _____   9. _____

5. _____   10. _____

You can add protein to your diet by consuming high quality protein bars (the more nutritious ones have at least 15 grams of protein per bar and have few fat, sugar and carbohydrate grams) and protein shakes. You can enhance the flavor of the shakes by mixing them in the blender with ice and a tablespoon or two of sugar-free, fat-free whipped topping, sugar-free flavored water packets, sugar-free pudding mix, etc.

2. Maintain portion control

One way post-surgical patients lose control of portion size is by grazing. Grazing is grazing, regardless of whether the food you put in your mouth is healthy or not. Grazing amounts to eating too much, not at one sitting but by eating bits of this here and bits of that there…throughout the day. Eating too many calories results in gaining weight. Period. It's important to eat at regular intervals so you keep track of when and how much you eat. When you graze or eat mindlessly, as when eating while watching television or reading, you aren't aware of how much food you consume. Even though your stomach pouch is the size of an egg, if you fill it continually all day long, you will consume a lot of food and a lot of calories over the course of a day. Eat your meals at prescribed times and be aware of making healthy food choices in sensible portions. Try setting a timer and don't eat anything for at least three hours after you've last eaten.

Have I been guilty of grazing? If so, when? What are (3) three ways in which I will implement healthy changes in order to avoid grazing from this point on?

1. _____

2. _____

3. _____

3. Exercise daily

Talk about a road infrequently traveled! In order to sustain your weight loss you must exercise on a consistent basis. No exceptions. No excuses.

Do I still make excuses for not exercising often enough? What are they and what are (3) three ways in which I will talk back to my excuses and/or be sure to get exercise more days than not?

1. _____

2. _____

3. _____

4. **Drink plenty of water throughout the day.**

   You need water to remain healthy – and you need quite a bit of it every day. Get into the habit of drinking water throughout the day. It's really not hard to do… just carry a bottle or cup of it wherever you go. Come on – you take your cell phone with you everywhere, and you use it, too! Do the same with water!

   What excuses have I made for not drinking enough water throughout the day? What are (3) three ways I will increase my water intake between meals?

   1. _____

   2. _____

   3. _____

5. **Eat breakfast**

   What's the big deal about eating breakfast? According to MayoClinic.com, "A healthy breakfast refuels your body and replenishes your blood sugar (glucose), giving you the energy necessary to start a new day. In addition, a growing body of evidence indicates that breakfast is good for both your physical and mental health." Breakfast is also important as it wakes your metabolism up after it, like you, has been sleeping during the night. You want to lose weight and keep it off, so get your metabolism running first thing in the morning. It has also been noted that eating breakfast increases your concentration and improves your thinking, leads to eating more nutritionally throughout the day, and increasing energy.

   What are the excuses I have made for not eating breakfast on a regular basis and what excuses have I made for eating unhealthy breakfasts? What are(3) three ways I will increase the consistency of eating healthy breakfast?

   1. _____

   2. _____

   3. _____

6. **Plan your meals and follow your plan.**

   I hear you groaning. I know…I know…it's hard, you don't have time, it takes a lot of effort, blah, blah, blah. When you went on various other diets, you planned meals. The problem was, when you "went off" the diet, you stopped planning your meals, and you stopped losing weight.

One of my favorite mottos is, "Work smarter, not harder." In this case, one way to do that is to keep your food plans on your computer. Once you have fifteen or twenty days of meals planned, you can mix and match. That doesn't take much time!

What are some excuses I have made for not keeping, and following meal plans? What are (3) three ways I can improve my habit of meal planning and following the plan?

1. _____

2. _____

3. _____

7. **Keep food and exercise journals**

This sounds like two different tasks. However, you would be wise to keep one journal where you record both your food and exercise for the day. (It's that "work smarter, not harder" concept again). It doesn't matter how you choose to journal. It matters that you choose to journal.

I can't emphasize just how important this is. There are so many reasons for you to record both what you eat and the amount of time and kind of exercise that you do. Maintaining food and exercise journals provides a measure of accountability. Writing down every bite of food that goes in your mouth prevents you from lying to yourself about what you have actually eaten.

Keeping a food diary may be the most beneficial tool you can use to maintain your weight loss. If you start gaining weight, you can look back in your journal and see what you are doing differently and what needs to change to stay on track. Your journals will also help strengthen your motivation. Take time each week and each month to review your eating behaviors. Give yourself credit for developing and maintaining healthy habits and for sticking to your plan. This, in turn, helps you build confidence. Seeing success increases your desire to continue succeeding.

While you're at it, it's a good idea to make yourself keep a weight graph, too. A graph is a great visual reminder that you are losing weight. When you reach the weight your body settles into, maintain the graph over time. If the line on the graph starts to rise, indicating an increase in your weight, it means you are doing something differently.

The goal is to keep your excess weight off. If you are regaining, review your food and exercise journals, discover where the problems lie, make a plan to "get back to the basics" (meaning doing what you did to lose the weight in the first place) and implement your plan.

With all of the new cell phone "apps," it's become increasing easier to record your food and exercise throughout the day. YES, YOU CAN do this! Choose to implement adult-like thinking and make up your mind that because you want good health, you are willing to do what is required to obtain it. GO YOU!

What are the excuses I have made for not maintaining food and exercise journals on a regular basis? What are (3) three ways I will increase the consistency of doing so?

1. _____

2. _____

3. _____

8. Get plenty of sleep

"Chronic sleep deprivation may cause weight gain by affecting the way our bodies process and store carbohydrates, and by altering levels of hormones that affect our appetite," as reported in the January 2006 edition of Harvard Women's Health Watch.

What are the excuses I have made for not getting enough sleep on a regular basis? What are (3) three ways I will increase the consistency of getting enough sleep (7+ hours each night)?

1. _____

2. _____

3. _____

9. Utilize a healthy support system (support group meetings and online support)

No one can do the work of weight loss for you; yet, you can't do it alone. You are the one who has to make the choice to lose weight and follow through with each of the Gotta Do Ems. Your spouse can't be responsible for what you put in your mouth. Your children can't be responsible for whether or not you exercise. Your friends can't make you keep a food and exercise journal. Only you can do these things. But you can't do it alone. You need encouragement, which your spouse, children, and friends can give you. You need education, which your doctor and nutritionist can give you. You need knowledge that comes from experience, which others who have been through the process can give you.

What are the excuses I have made for not utilizing a healthy support system? What are (3) three ways I will do so?

1. _____

2. _____

3. _____

10. **Participate in individual and/or group counseling**

Those of you who are the most serious about keeping your weight off will pick up the phone and make an appointment with a qualified therapist right now, if you haven't been attending therapy already. Those of you who think you don't need this are fooling yourselves. Can you lose weight without attending therapy? Of course! Can you keep your weight off without attending therapy? Perhaps, but I have seen and heard with my own eyes and ears the stories of people just like you (and don't forget, I am a recovering addict). I know about the issues underlying addiction, and how hard they are to change. I have been to therapy myself. I know firsthand the benefits of having a professional help you work through the issues underneath your "problem."

What are (3) three excuses I have made for not participating in therapy? What are (3) three ways I can work through my resistance? (And remember, cost is not a valid reason; there are many therapy agencies who provide free and reduced-cost sessions.)

1. _____

2. _____

3. _____

Recovery from obesity following bariatric surgery is about learning to live life on life's terms; learning to deal with your thoughts and feelings without using food to alleviate sadness, pain, anger, loneliness, or boredom. Work with your therapist to break your bad eating habits and learn new, healthy habits. Let a professional teach you how to recognize negative, sabotaging thoughts, and replace them with helpful ways of thinking and behaving. Losing weight is difficult. Keeping it off, even more so. Give yourself a gift and get into therapy. You'll be amazed at how much better you feel every time you leave a session (even if you leave in tears)! You will also have balance in each and every one of your Centers much sooner than someone not attending therapy.

The Goals

As you finish this book, my hope for you is that your goals following weight loss surgery include:

- Losing your excess weight

- **KEEPING THE EXCESS WEIGHT OFF FOR A LIFETIME**

- Improving your overall health

- Living a full, balanced life in your Spiritual Center, your Cognitive Center, your Emotional Center, your Physical Center, your Social Center, and your Enterprise Center.

Many people don't know how to set goals, other than to say, "I'm gonna do this or I'm gonna do that." It may be a start to verbalize what you want to do. But saying so may not get you very far. The following is a worksheet you can use to set goals for yourself. Update it often!

Goals Form

The first half of this form is designed to help you focus your thoughts. The second half is specific to setting goals.

AM I THE PERSON I WANT TO BE? Describing Me

Words/phrases I would like my spouse to use when describing me:

_____

Words/phrases I would like my children to use when describing me:

_____

Words/phrases I would like any employees I might have to use when describing me:

_____

Words/phrases I would like my friends to use when describing me:

_____

In one sentence, using the information from above, "How I would like to describe myself/ who do I want to be?": _____

_____

When I die, here is where I would like to be in terms of my:
SPIRITUALITY: _____

_____

RELATIONSHIPS: (Spouse/Significant Other, Family, Friends) _____

_____

WORK: _____

_____

MONEY: (Short-term and Long-term) _____

_____

HEALTH: (Weight, Fitness, Nutrition, Physical Health, and Emotional Health)

_____

_____

Goals Form (Continued)

For each of the following areas, over the next 12 months, I will attain the following goals in these *specific and measurable ways*. **Example**: A specific and measurable way to meet a spiritual goal would be: *"I will set aside 30 minutes for quiet self-reflection and journaling three days each week."*

SPIRITUALITY: _____

_____

How I will attain this goal (specific/measurable): _____

_____

RELATIONSHIPS: (Spouse/Significant Other, Family, Friends) _____

_____

_____

How I will attain this goal (specific/measurable): _____

_____

WORK: _____

_____

How I will attain this goal (specific/measurable): _____

_____

MONEY: (Short-term and Long-term) _____

_____

_____

How I will attain this goal (specific/measurable): _____

_____

HEALTH: (Weight, Fitness, Nutrition, Physical Health, and Emotional Health)

_____

_____

How I will attain this goal (specific/measurable): _____

_____

_____

When you have completed this worksheet, use it to help you realize these goals. Read your goals regularly – daily, if possible. This will lead you to follow through with your goals! Try it – I think you'll be pleased with the results!

Establishing New Habits

Establishing healthy new habits goes hand-in-hand with goal-setting, so this would be a good time to talk about habits! My good friend and business partner in A Post Op & A Doc (APOD) is Cari De La Cruz. Cari had gastric bypass surgery in 2007. She refers to herself as "twice the woman in half the body," which I think is fun ... and accurate! As A Post Op & A Doc, Cari and I create and present many ideas to help people in their recoveries from obesity. In fact, we developed a "recipe" for recovery! It consists of the following ingredients:

Awareness *(The first step in change)*

Acceptance *(Willing to make changes)*

Commitment (Determination to do the changes)

Accountability (Doing the changes)

Attitude (Staying positive while making the changes)

Effort (Keep on doing what needs to be done)

In considering writing about how to establish these new habits, which you'll have to do when incorporating the Gotta Do Ems into your life; I immediately thought about APOD's Recipe for Recovery. You can use these same ingredients to establish new habits. I'll work through an example for you, and then you can use this same process in developing whatever good new habits you want to incorporate into your life.

Habit to develop and incorporate: *Exercise on a regular basis.*

1: AWARENESS (The first step in change)

- I am aware that I don't exercise on a regular basis.
- I've been made aware in the educational process of my weight loss surgery that consistent exercise is necessary for sustained weight loss.

2: ACCEPTANCE (Willingness to make changes)

- I accept that regular exercise is necessary in my life because I want to maintain a healthy weight.
- I accept that I need to make exercise a regular part of my life on a regular basis in order to maintain a healthy weight.
- I accept that I need to make changes in my life (schedule, relationships, attitude) in order to follow through with a regular exercise routine.

3: COMMITMENT (Determination to make the changes)

- I am making the following commitments to demonstrate my determination to establish the habit of regular exercise:
  - I commit to shortening my lunch break at work to 30 minutes so I can go to the gym on my way home Mon-Thurs and still get home to my family by 6 PM.
  - I commit to going to the gym immediately after work Monday – Thursday.
  - I commit to keeping my work-out clothes in the car so I can go straight to the gym.
  - I commit to paying for a personal trainer two days a week while I am at the gym.
  - I will walk for a minimum of two miles at least one time on the weekend.

4. ACCOUNTABILITY (Doing the changes)

- I will maintain accountability for going to the gym by:
  - setting an alarm on my phone both at lunch time (to remind me of my 30 minute lunch and to remind me of my commitment to going to the gym) AND I will set an alarm on my phone when it is time for me to be in the gym using the equipment
  - sharing with my family at dinner about what I accomplished at the gym each day
  - noting the specifics of my workout on my exercise log

5. ATTITUDE (Staying positive while making the changes)

- I will maintain a positive attitude about going to the gym by:
  - reminding myself of the following benefits when any negative thoughts about going to the gym enter my mind:
    - my improved health
    - the progress I make in my workout ability
    - the fact that my clothing fits better and I wear smaller sizes
    - my increase in energy
    - my better attitude at work and at home
    - rewarding myself every week I follow my exercise plan by:
      - allowing myself to spend $XX on new clothing
      - playfully bragging to my husband, who is very supportive of me, about my progress
      - at the end of every month that I have maintained my exercise schedule, I will allow myself to buy an additional $XX of clothes, shoes or accessories.

- I will resume my work-out schedule immediately if I miss a day and will get support to keep going in the following ways:
  - talk with my support group friends about ways I'm harming myself by not going to the gym
  - talk with my therapist about my disappointment in self
  - read on the internet
- I will post notes that encourage and remind me about the benefits of my workouts at home and at work

6. EFFORT (Keep on doing what needs to be done)
- I will do the following to help sustain my effort:
  - ask my best friend to remind me of the reasons I want to exercise (health, attitude, new clothes!)
  - go to support groups and share with others how regular exercise is benefitting me
  - make a benefits board where I post pictures of my progress in terms of weight loss, positive quotes, goals, etc.
  - talk with a therapist if I struggle to follow through with my commitment to exercise on a regular basis

It can be difficult to get started with healthy new habits and difficult to stick with them. The bottom line really is, "What do I want more? What I had (no exercise, in the case of our example and as a result of no exercise… poor physical condition, lack of energy, lack of belief in self (ability, worth), etc. versus what I say I want (increased energy, more positive thinking, and the ability to do more things I've been wanting to do)? It's your choice. It's not easy. No one can do this for you, but you can do it with the help and support of others. And the effort IS worth the outcome. Improved health and a better quality of life as a result of losing weight and keeping it off by practicing healthy habits is a gift that you give to yourself and share with so many others!

Always remember: **"MY HEALTH, MY RESPONSIBIITY…THIS DAY. EVERY DAY."** It might sound trite, but living one day at a time is a great way to live. Staying in the day, not worrying about tomorrow, next week or next year, has saved many a recovering alcoholic a trip down hangover lane. It can save you a trip there yourself, whether it be a hangover from alcohol, too much food, or from a night of self-pity and anger.

Gratefully Yours

You have taken a lot of time to read these pages, complete the exercises provided, and think about your life. I hope that you have learned things about what you need for your own personal recovery from obesity in the years ahead as you keep your weight off -one day at a time.

I wrote **Eat It Up!** and subsequently this companion Workbook as much for myself as for you. I know the importance of sharing what I have learned along my journey in recovery. What comes out of my mouth or my mind is not necessarily original (I've read most of it or been taught it by others), but my way of passing it on has originality. So many people, who have shared with me their wisdom, strength, experiences - and sometimes a swift kick to my rear - have helped to bless my life in so many ways. Hopefully, by my sharing these words, you will take what you need and put them to good use. We all need to remember… **"I am responsible for the effort that I put into whatever I do."** Your health is, after all, your responsibility. This day. Every day.

With gratitude to you, I close this chapter and this Workbook, as I closed **Eat It Up!**, leaving with you the theme of my life's work through a quote from George Herbert:

> *Give Thanks. Thou Who has given us so much.*
> *Mercifully grant us one more thing— a grateful heart.*
> **George Herbert** (1593-1633)

For **gratitude**, I believe, is the key to happiness.

Made in the USA
Columbia, SC
06 May 2024

35364390R00096